**Improve your bridge game—
the entertaining way.**

♠

All the puzzles in this book contain hands that you
might hold in your next game.

♥

Tackle them as though you were sitting around a
bridge table and could see only your own hand.
Then bid and play as both declarer and defender.

♦

Not only will you have fun, but you'll learn a great
deal about bridge in the process.

♣

DEVYN PRESS BOOK OF BRIDGE PUZZLES #1
(Originally Titled "Pocket Book of Bridge Puzzles #1")

DEVYN PRESS BOOK OF BRIDGE PUZZLES #1 IS A REPRINT OF THE
POCKET BOOK OF BRIDGE PUZZLES #1
Pocket Book edition published June, 1970
DEVYN PRESS EDITION PUBLISHED JANUARY, 1981

Standard Book Number: 671-75475-0

PRINTED IN THE UNITED STATES OF AMERICA

Manufactured in the U.S.A.
    Devyn Press
    1327 Walnut St.
    Shelbyville, KY 40065

DEVYN PRESS BOOK OF

BRIDGE PUZZLES

NUMBER

1

by Alfred Sheinwold

(Originally Titled Pocket Book Of Bridge Puzzles #1)

Devyn Press
Shelbyville, Kentucky

Cover by
Bonnie J. Baron

Introduction

The puzzles in this book are all bridge hands that might be dealt out in your next game. They are meant for your entertainment, but they will also improve your game—quite painlessly.

Tackle them as though you held the hands in an actual bridge game. You would see only your own hand during the bidding; and you would see only your own hand and the dummy during the play of the cards. It's true that here you can see *all* of the cards, but you'll miss part of the fun if you peek. After all, you wouldn't be able to see an opponent's hand during an actual game of bridge. (If you can, you don't need a bridge book; but you may need a doctor some day.)

First, notice the dealer and the vulnerability and try to work out reasonable bidding for each player—just as you think it might go in a good expert game. The players use what is often called "Standard American" bidding methods, with Blackwood and Stayman, but no other fancy conventions. You have one good clue to all of the contracts: South is always the declarer. When you have decided upon the right bids for each player, write them at the bottom of the hand—in the spaces provided for this. Pick West's best opening lead also—not a "peeking" opening lead, but the lead he would probably make if he could see only his own hand. Then write that down.

Now you can try to play the hand. Take a light pencil and draw a slim slanting line through each card as you play it. Don't act with a knowledge of all four hands; assume that each player can see only his own hand and the dummy—just as in an actual game. Declarer should usually make his contract by proper play—but, since you are both declarer and defender, always try to defeat the contract by logical play.

Take the hand below, for example. Let's assume that you got to six spades by some logical bidding and that you chose the actual opening lead of the jack of clubs. Take the play from that point on.

NORTH
♠ Q 3 2
♡ Q 4
◇ Q J 10 9
♣ A K 6 2

WEST　　　　　　　　　　　EAST
♠ 8　　　　　　　　　　　♠ 10 9 7
♡ J 9 8 7　　　　　　　♡ K 6
◇ K 6 5 2　　　　　　　◇ 8 7 4 3
♣ J 10 9 8　　　　　　　♣ Q 7 5 3

SOUTH-D
♠ A K J 6 5 4
♡ A 10 5 3 2
◇ A
♣ 4

SOUTH	WEST	NORTH	EAST
1 ♠	Pass	2 ♣	Pass
3 ♡	Pass	4 ♠	Pass
5 ◇	Pass	5 ♡	Pass
6 ♠	All Pass		

Draw a slanting line through West's jack of clubs and win the trick in dummy with the king of clubs. Now slant through the king also. Slant through East's five of clubs (he begins an "encouraging" signal) and through the four of clubs in the South hand.

Let's suppose you plan to set up the hearts. You cash dummy's ace of clubs, discarding a heart, get to your hand with the ace of diamonds and lead a heart to dummy's queen. Draw a slanting line (as in the diagram) through all of these cards.

East wins the queen of hearts with the king and returns a club to make you use up a trump. Now you take the ace of hearts and ruff a heart with dummy's queen of trumps.

This plan would work if West had the king of hearts, if the

2

jack of hearts fell early or if East had only one trump instead of three.

But you see what is going to happen. You can't do anything with that ten of hearts. Sooner or later you will lose the setting trick either to West's jack of hearts or to one of East's trumps. Down you go at six spades.

Some players prefer to skip playing the hand based on their own bidding and selection of the opening lead. Instead, after doing their own bidding, they turn to the bidding as shown at the top of the right-hand page and use the opening lead shown there. Then they proceed with their own play of the hand by making a slanting line as each trick is played. When the hand is over, they then read what happened in the hand.

You can even make *two* games out of each hand by putting a circle around each card as it is played the second time, in addition to the slanting line used during the first play of the hand.

Now you're ready to see how South made six spades in our illustrative hand. After winning the first trick with the king of clubs, declarer led dummy's ace of clubs and discarded the ace of diamonds!

With this card out of the way, declarer led the queen of diamonds and discarded a heart. West could take the king of diamonds, but regardless of the return South won and drew trumps with the ace, king and queen in that order.

South was now in the dummy with the trumps drawn. He ran the rest of dummy's diamonds, discarding his other low hearts. The rest of the tricks were easily his with the ace of hearts and his remaining trumps.

Now you are ready for the puzzles. I envy you the fun of seeing these hands for the first time!

ALFRED SHEINWOLD

Don't Expect to Win with Best Play

"Keep your head down, and don't look up during the bidding or play," a friend of mine advised his wife during a recent bridge game. "It doesn't do anything for her game," he whispered to me, "but it stops her from seeing the look on my face." The lady had just played the hand shown below.

South dealer   **Both sides vulnerable**

NORTH
♠ 6 5 3
♡ K 7
◇ J 10 9 8 5
♣ K 8 4

WEST   EAST
♠ J 10 9 4   ♠ 8 7 2
♡ 10 9 5   ♡ Q J 8 4
◇ K 7 6 3   ◇ 4
♣ 7 3   ♣ J 10 9 5 2

SOUTH-D
♠ A K Q
♡ A 6 3 2
◇ A Q 2
♣ A Q 6

Defense Tricks:

☐ ☐ ☐ ☐ ☐ ☐ ☐ ☐ ☐ ☐ ☐ ☐ ☐

Bid the hand your way:

North	East	South	West
———	———	———	———
———	———	———	———
———	———	———	———
———	———	———	———
		Opening Lead ———	

4

How the hand was bid:

SOUTH	WEST	NORTH	EAST
3 NT	Pass	4 NT	Pass
6 NT	All Pass		

Opening lead — ♠ J

How the hand was played: South took the queen of spades, led a heart to dummy's king and returned the jack of diamonds for a finesse. I played low from the West hand.

Our heroine continued with dummy's low diamond. My partner (and wife) discarded a spade from the East hand. South put up the ace of diamonds and continued with the queen of diamonds. I refused the trick again.

Now South had three diamond tricks but could not get a fourth. She could get to dummy with the king of clubs to set up another diamond, but then she would never get back to dummy for the good diamond.

South eventually had to give up two hearts. Down one. ⌐

NOTHING WRONG

There was nothing wrong with leading a heart to dummy's king and returning the jack of diamonds from dummy. But South must finesse with the queen of diamonds (in case East has only K-x), continue with the ace and then lead the deuce of diamonds.

It is a cinch to set up the diamonds with the king of clubs as an entry. South gets four diamond tricks instead of only three, making the slam.

As the hand was actually played, my defense was simple but correct. I expected no medals for it, but I certainly didn't expect to be scolded. Unfortunately, my wife heard my friend's whispered explanation of his advice.

"Husbands!" she hissed at me. Sometimes there's no way to win even if you make the right play.

Norwegian Play Still Discussed

When bridge players gather for a tournament the early arrivals usually sit around discussing the best hands they have seen. They still talk about a hand played in the 1933 European Championships by Johannes Brun, a member of the Norwegian team that year.

North dealer   **North-South vulnerable**

NORTH-D
♠ A K 8 5 3
♡ Q 4
♢ 2
♣ A K 6 5 2

WEST
♠ J 9 2
♡ 8 6
♢ A K 10 9 8 5
♣ Q 7

EAST
♠ Q 10 7 6
♡ A 9 3
♢ Q
♣ J 10 9 8 3

SOUTH
♠ 4
♡ K J 10 7 5 2
♢ J 7 6 4 3
♣ 4

Defense Tricks:

☐ ☐ ☐ ☐ ☐ ☐ ☐ ☐ ☐ ☐ ☐ ☐ ☐

Bid the hand your way:

North	East	South	West
_____	_____	_____	_____
_____	_____	_____	_____
_____	_____	_____	_____
_____	_____	_____	_____
		Opening Lead	_____

How the hand was bid:

NORTH	EAST	SOUTH	WEST
1 ♣	Pass	1 ♡	2 ◊
2 ♠	Pass	3 ♡	Pass
4 ♡	All Pass		

Opening lead — ◊ K

How the hand was played: West opened the king of diamonds and stopped short when East dropped the queen. South obviously had the rest of the diamonds and would be delighted to ruff one or two of them in dummy. To stop this, West shifted to a trump.

East took the ace of trumps and returned a trump. South was now limited to nine tricks: five trumps and the four top cards in spades and clubs. There were not enough entries to the dummy to set up and cash a long card in either black suit.

Brun did not say die. He took the second round of trumps with the king and continued with the jack of hearts to draw East's last trump. He had to discard a spade or a club from dummy on the third trump and wisely chose to throw a club on the theory that if either opponent had five or more spades he would have entered the bidding with a spade bid.

GOES AFTER SPADES

Brun next went after the spades by taking the ace and king and ruffing a spade. Then he returned to dummy with the king of clubs and led another spade. East played the queen, and declarer discarded a diamond.

East had only clubs left and had to lead one of them to dummy's ace. This put Brun back in the dummy so that he could cash the tenth trick—the last spade.

Barbarous Finesses Astonish Kibitzer

The Old Kibitzer tottered out of the card room of his club in a state of near-shock. "They take all the wrong finesses," he muttered. "The game has fallen into the hands of barbarians."

East dealer   **Both sides vulnerable**

NORTH
♠ J 5
♡ A 8 7
◇ J 5 4
♣ K Q J 10 3

WEST   EAST-D
♠ K 7 6 2   ♠ A Q 9 8 3
♡ 5   ♡ K 6 2
◇ 8 7 6 2   ◇ K 10 9 3
♣ 9 7 6 4   ♣ 8

SOUTH
♠ 10 4
♡ Q J 10 9 4 3
◇ A Q
♣ A 5 2

Defense Tricks:

☐ ☐ ☐ ☐ ☐ ☐ ☐ ☐ ☐ ☐ ☐ ☐ ☐

Bid the hand your way:

North	East	South	West
_____	_____	_____	_____
_____	_____	_____	_____
_____	_____	_____	_____
_____	_____	_____	_____
		Opening Lead	_____

How the hand was bid:

EAST	SOUTH	WEST	NORTH
1 ♠	2 ♡	2 ♠	4 ♡
All Pass			

Opening lead — ♠ 2

How the hand was played: The Old Kibitzer gulped when he saw East play the queen of spades at the first trick. East returned the singleton club, which rode to dummy's ten.

The old gentleman had expected South to win the club in his own hand in order to try the trump finesse. South would draw trumps and discard his losers on dummy's clubs. He would never have to try the diamond finesse.

Instead, declarer won the club in dummy and returned a diamond to try a finesse with the queen. This was when the Old Kibitzer ran from the room.

Oddly enough, all of the barbarous finesses were correct. East "finessed" with the queen of spades at the first trick to see if his partner had the king. When he found out, East could afford to return his singleton club.

COUNTERS DEFENSE

South could not afford to take the trump finesse against this defense. East would take the king of hearts and return a spade to the king. Back would come a club, and East's ruff would defeat the contract.

Instead, South took the diamond finesse, cashed the ace of diamonds and led a trump to dummy's ace (refusing the only finesse that the Old Kibitzer would have taken). Then he led the jack of diamonds from dummy and discarded the ten of spades from his hand when East put up the king of diamonds.

This gave up a diamond instead of a spade, but it was more than an even exchange. East could not get the lead to his partner and therefore couldn't get a club ruff. South's contract was safe.

Choose Right Time to Feed Opponent

Biting the hand that feeds you is called vicious—by feeders; but it seems very normal to all biters. If you're going to feed a known biter, don't be foolish enough to put your hand in with the food. And if you're wondering what this has to do with bridge, play the hand below.

South dealer   **Both sides vulnerable**

                                        NORTH
                                        ♠ A K 4 3
                                        ♡ Q 4
                                        ◇ 6 5 3 2
                                        ♣ J 5 2

            WEST   EAST
            ♠ 9   ♠ 10 8 7 6 5 2
            ♡ 8 6   ♡ J 10 9 7
            ◇ K J 9 8   ◇ 7 4
            ♣ 10 9 8 7 4 3   ♣ 6

                                        SOUTH-D
                                        ♠ Q J
                                        ♡ A K 5 3 2
                                        ◇ A Q 10
                                        ♣ A K Q

Defense Tricks:

☐ ☐ ☐ ☐ ☐ ☐ ☐ ☐ ☐ ☐ ☐ ☐ ☐ ☐

Bid the hand your way:

North	East	South	West
_____	_____	_____	_____
_____	_____	_____	_____
_____	_____	_____	_____
_____	_____	_____	_____
		Opening Lead	_____

How the hand was bid:

SOUTH	WEST	NORTH	EAST
2 ♡	Pass	2 ♠	Pass
3 NT	Pass	6 NT	All Pass

Opening lead — ♣ 10

How the hand was played: South won the first trick with the queen of clubs, cleared the queen and jack of spades out of the way and went to dummy with the queen of hearts. He discarded two diamonds on the ace and king of spades and then went after the hearts.

The plan was very reasonable. South could get four heart tricks if the suit broke either 3-3 or 4-2. The odds were 5 to 1 in his favor—far better than discarding two hearts on the spades and hoping for a successful finesse in diamonds.

Unfortunately, East had a heart stopper and two good spades. If South continued the hearts, East would take three tricks. South had to be content with taking the first eleven tricks, but he was still down one.

RIGHT TIME

The hand is unbeatable if South gives up a heart trick before he has developed the setting trick for East.

After taking two high clubs and the queen and jack of spades, South should play a low heart from each hand. This gives the opponents their food, but South is safe against all possible bites.

If East takes the heart trick and returns a diamond (the best defense), South steps up with the ace of diamonds and leads a heart to dummy's queen. He discards two diamonds on the high spades and returns to his hand with a club to run the rest of the tricks.

11

Don't Steal Your Own Property

Sometimes you can get the opponents to discard badly when you lead out a long string of trumps. Adopt this plan when you have nothing surer.

South dealer   **East-West vulnerable**

```
                    NORTH
                    ♠ 9 4 3
                    ♡ 10 9 8
                    ◇ Q 10 9 3
                    ♣ 7 5 2

      WEST                              EAST
      ♠ 10 8                            ♠ K Q J 5 2
      ♡ 7 6 3                           ♡ None
      ◇ A K J 8 5                       ◇ 7 6 4 2
      ♣ Q 8 3                           ♣ K J 10 9

                    SOUTH-D
                    ♠ A 7 6
                    ♡ A K Q J 5 4 2
                    ◇ None
                    ♣ A 6 4
```

Defense Tricks:

☐ ☐ ☐ ☐ ☐ ☐ ☐ ☐ ☐ ☐ ☐ ☐ ☐

Bid the hand your way:

North	East	South	West
_____	_____	_____	_____
_____	_____	_____	_____
_____	_____	_____	_____
_____	_____	_____	_____
		Opening Lead	_____

12

How the hand was bid:

SOUTH	WEST	NORTH	EAST
2 ♡	Pass	2 NT	Pass
3 ♡	Pass	3 NT	Pass
4 ♡	All Pass		

Opening lead — ◊ K

How the hand was played: South ruffed the king of diamonds and saw no legitimate way to avoid the loss of two tricks in each black suit. Rather than give up without a struggle, South led out his trumps in the hope that some weird problem might cause an opponent to throw the wrong cards.

It didn't work. East decided to keep three cards in each black suit, which turned out to be just right. If South had held four of one black suit and two of the other, he would have had a chance. As it was, he eventually lost two spades and two clubs. Down one.

South would have made the contract if he hadn't tried to steal a tenth trick that already belonged to him. He had nine sure tricks to start with and could have developed one of dummy's diamonds as his tenth trick.

RUFF HIGH

South must ruff the first trick with a high trump and lead a low trump to dummy's eight. He then leads a diamond from dummy and discards any low black card—say a spade.

West wins with the jack of diamonds and returns a club to force out the ace. South leads a trump to dummy's nine and gives up another diamond, discarding a club this time.

West wins with the ace of diamonds and cashes a club trick. South wins the next trick, whatever it is, and leads his last low trump to dummy's ten. Now he can cash dummy's last diamond and throw a spade away, making the game contract.

Take Your Time with Grand Slam

A careful bridge player guards against collapse of the brain cells by playing difficult hands as quickly as possible. This hurts only when he writes the score in the opponents' column. The technique is seen in action in the following hand.

North dealer   **Both sides vulnerable**

NORTH-D
♠ 3 2
♡ K 9 8 3
◇ A Q 10
♣ K 7 4 2

WEST   EAST
♠ J 9 8 5   ♠ 7 6
♡ 7 6   ♡ 5 4 2
◇ 9 8 7 6   ◇ K J 5 3 2
♣ Q 10 8   ♣ 6 5 3

SOUTH
♠ A K Q 10 4
♡ A Q J 10
◇ 4
♣ A J 9

Defense Tricks:

☐ ☐ ☐ ☐ ☐ ☐ ☐ ☐ ☐ ☐ ☐ ☐

Bid the hand your way:

North	East	South	West
———	———	———	———
———	———	———	———
———	———	———	———
———	———	———	———
		Opening Lead ———	

How the hand was bid:

NORTH	EAST	SOUTH	WEST
Pass	Pass	1 ♠	Pass
2 NT	Pass	3 ♡	Pass
4 ♡	Pass	5 ♣	Pass
5 ◊	Pass	7 ♡	All Pass

Opening lead — ◊ 9

How the hand was played: Declarer took the ace of diamonds, drew three rounds of trumps and led out the top spades, discarding a club from dummy. Since the jack of spades had not dropped, South had to ruff a spade with dummy's last trump and then had to stake the grand slam on the club finesse.

West defeated the contract with the queen of clubs, and South smugly announced: "No score. We had honors."

Since the entire performance had taken two minutes, South was able to go to the next hand with the feeling that he had wasted very little time.

South could have scored 2,310 points if he had taken one additional minute to play the hand. This news will interest only those bridge players who are willing to work for a couple of thousand points per minute.

RUFF DIAMONDS

After taking the ace of diamonds South should ruff a diamond. He cashes the ace of hearts, overtakes a heart with dummy's king to ruff another diamond and leads a club to dummy's king to draw the last trump with dummy's nine. Since South is out of trumps, he discards the jack of clubs on the nine of hearts.

Now South cashes the top spades, ruffs a spade with dummy's last trump and gets to his hand with the ace of clubs to take the last trick with the ten of spades.

Not very difficult, not very slow, but very productive.

Say Right Thing at End of Hand

Many players flounder when the play of a hand comes to an end. What is the right thing to say to partner? Where will you find advice on this nice point of etiquette?

South dealer   **Both sides vulnerable**

NORTH
♠ Q 10 4 2
♡ Q 2
◇ A 7 3
♣ A 10 7 6

WEST   EAST
♠ 6   ♠ J 9 8
♡ A K J 10 7 6   ♡ 8 3
◇ Q J 9 8   ◇ 6 5 2
♣ J 2   ♣ Q 9 8 5 3

SOUTH-D
♠ A K 7 5 3
♡ 9 5 4
◇ K 10 4
♣ K 4

Defense Tricks:

☐ ☐ ☐ ☐ ☐ ☐ ☐ ☐ ☐ ☐ ☐ ☐ ☐

Bid the hand your way:

North	East	South	West
_____	_____	_____	_____
_____	_____	_____	_____
_____	_____	_____	_____
_____	_____	_____	_____
		Opening Lead _____	

How the hand was bid:

SOUTH	WEST	NORTH	EAST
1 ♠	2 ♡	3 ♠	Pass
4 ♠	All Pass		

Opening lead — ♡ K

How the hand was played: Imagine yourself the dummy in today's hand, watching your partner go down at four spades. West takes the king and ace of hearts, and East signals for a continuation by playing the eight of hearts first and then the three.

West continues with the jack of hearts, and your partner studies the dummy very carefully. The careful study does not deceive you, for South is wondering whether to ruff with dummy's queen or with dummy's ten of trumps.

South is calculating that the ten of spades has an even chance to shut East out. The queen of spades will work perhaps 52 percent of the time, since the jack will drop singleton or doubleton about that often.

EITHER WILL FAIL

You keep a straight face, knowing that either plan will fail. Finally, you partner ruffs with dummy's ten of spades. East overruffs with the jack, and your partner eventually loses a diamond trick. Down one.

What do you say to your partner? The correct thing is: "Please cut the cards for the next deal." Then close your teeth tightly together and look at your fingernails. It is considered poor form to punch your partner in the nose, even though he did throw a cold hand away.

South should not ruff the jack of hearts at all. Instead, he should throw a diamond from the dummy. Then he can win any continuation, draw trumps and ruff his third diamond in dummy. But keep it to yourself; maybe your partner will be equally restrained when you're the villain of the piece.

17

Classic Crime of Noble Declarer

"Present-day crimes don't intrigue me," Sherlock Holmes complained. "Where would you see nowadays a crime like the hand played by Lord Grenoc in the Nichevo Cup finals thirty years ago?"

South dealer   **Neither side vulnerable**

NORTH
♠ J 10 2
♡ 6 5
◇ K Q J 10 4
♣ J 10 3

<table>
<tr><td>WEST</td><td>EAST</td></tr>
<tr><td>♠ Q 8 7 3</td><td>♠ 9 6 4</td></tr>
<tr><td>♡ 10 9 3</td><td>♡ 7</td></tr>
<tr><td>◇ 8 7</td><td>◇ A 9 6 5 3 2</td></tr>
<tr><td>♣ K 7 4 2</td><td>♣ 9 8 5</td></tr>
</table>

SOUTH-D
♠ A K 5
♡ A K Q J 8 4 2
◇ None
♣ A Q 6

Defense Tricks:

☐ ☐ ☐ ☐ ☐ ☐ ☐ ☐ ☐ ☐ ☐ ☐ ☐ ☐

Bid the hand your way:

North	East	South	West
_____	_____	_____	_____
_____	_____	_____	_____
_____	_____	_____	_____
_____	_____	_____	_____

Opening Lead _____

How the hand was bid:

SOUTH	WEST	NORTH	EAST
2 ♡	Pass	3 ◊	Pass
3 ♡	Pass	3 NT	Pass
6 ♡	All Pass		

Opening lead — ◊ 8

How the hand was played: "His Lordship ruffed the ace of diamonds, drew trumps and led out the ace and queen of clubs," Holmes reminisced.

"West refused the trick, of course?" Dr. Watson asked anxiously.

"Of course. This was no vulgar mugging. Grenoc then led his low club. West took the king of clubs and got out safely with his last club."

"So his Lordship had to lose a spade trick?" the good Doctor asked.

"Obviously," Holmes snapped. "What a classic crime. To mangle the hand of a lifetime!"

WATSON AGREES

"Quite so," Watson agreed. "Ahem. He should have led a low spade before touching the clubs, and he'd have caught West quite off balance."

"He wasn't playing against children," Holmes observed dryly. "You don't seem to be much better than his Lordship."

South must ruff the first diamond with a high heart. Then he leads out the ace and king of hearts and continues with the deuce of hearts. West is forced to win (even if he has been careful to drop the nine and ten), and any return puts dummy in the lead to give declarer discards on the diamonds.

Test Your Honesty with Hand

Try playing the bridge hand below without peeking at the East-West cards. The average reader of this book wouldn't dream of peeking if asked not to—except perhaps at just a key card or two. Test yourself to see how honest you are.

North dealer   **North-South vulnerable**

NORTH-D
- ♠ K 8
- ♡ K 4 3
- ◇ A 6
- ♣ A 7 6 5 3 2

WEST
- ♠ 6 5 3 2
- ♡ Q J 10 9
- ◇ 7 3
- ♣ Q 9 8

EAST
- ♠ Q 4
- ♡ A 8 7 2
- ◇ 9 8 5 2
- ♣ K J 10

SOUTH
- ♠ A J 10 9 7
- ♡ 6 5
- ◇ K Q J 10 4
- ♣ 4

Defense Tricks:

☐ ☐ ☐ ☐ ☐ ☐ ☐ ☐ ☐ ☐ ☐ ☐ ☐

Bid the hand your way:

North	East	South	West
_____	_____	_____	_____
_____	_____	_____	_____
_____	_____	_____	_____
_____	_____	_____	_____

Opening Lead _____

How the hand was bid:

NORTH	EAST	SOUTH	WEST
1 ♣	Pass	1 ♠	Pass
1 NT	Pass	3 ◇	Pass
3 ♠	Pass	4 ♠	All Pass
			Opening lead — ♡ Q

How the hand was played: West leads the queen of hearts and continues the suit until you ruff the third round. Now you lead a spade to dummy's king and return a spade. East has to play the queen, so you draw all of the trumps and take eleven tricks.

There's nothing to the hand, of course. But we have discovered that you are a careless bridge player — or that you peeked at the spades.

Try exchanging the queen and six of spades and see what happens when you lead out the king and ace of spades. You will then have just the J-10 of spades, and West will have the Q-5. If you drive out the queen by playing the jack of spades, West will lead another heart to force out your last trump. Then you are sure to go down.

SAFE PLAY

The safe play for the contract is to ruff the third heart and lead the jack of spades for an immediate finesse. If East can win the trick and return a heart, dummy will ruff with the king of spades. Now you get to your hand with a diamond to draw the rest of the trumps.

If West had four spades to the queen, your jack of spades would win the first round of trumps. You continue with a trump to the king, cash the ace and king of diamonds, and draw one more trump with the ace. Then you lead out good diamonds, allowing West to take his high trump whenever he likes.

A careful player makes only ten tricks with this hand, but he is sure of his contract without having to peek.

Test Players with Difficult Slam

Use the following hand to test the skill and the good nature of your friends. Show them only the dummy and the South hand, and ask them to plan the play at six spades against a club lead. Promise them that no suit breaks very badly.

North dealer   **East-West vulnerable**

NORTH-D

♠ A K 8
♡ A K 9 8 7 2
◇ Q 6
♣ A Q

WEST   EAST

♠ J 10 3   ♠ 9
♡ 5 4   ♡ Q J 10 6
◇ 8 4   ◇ K J 10 9
♣ J 9 7 5 4 2   ♣ K 10 6 3

SOUTH

♠ Q 7 6 5 4 2
♡ 3
◇ A 7 5 3 2
♣ 8

Defense Tricks:

☐ ☐ ☐ ☐ ☐ ☐ ☐ ☐ ☐ ☐ ☐ ☐ ☐ ☐

Bid the hand your way:

North	East	South	West
_____	_____	_____	_____
_____	_____	_____	_____
_____	_____	_____	_____
_____	_____	_____	_____
		Opening Lead	_____

How the hand was bid:

NORTH	EAST	SOUTH	WEST
2 ♡	Pass	2 NT	Pass
3 ♡	Pass	3 ♠	Pass
4 ♠	Pass	6 ♠	All Pass

Opening lead — ♣ 5

How the hand was played: Declarer should not expect any very lucky breaks. The four missing spades should break 3-1 rather than 2-2. Likewise, the six missing cards in each red suit should break 4-2 rather than 3-3.

Given this information, your victim should be able to make six spades. But he won't if you catch him before he has read this column.

The correct play is to win the first trick with dummy's ace of clubs and immediately return the key from dummy: a low heart!

East wins and leads the king of clubs. South ruffs, cashes the queen and king of spades and ruffs a low heart.

NO OVERRUFF

Since this is only the second round of hearts, there is no danger of an overruff. (You promised that no suit breaks very badly.)

South leads a trump to dummy's ace, drawing the last trump. He then cashes the ace and king of hearts, after which dummy's two low hearts are good. South throws four diamonds on these four hearts, after which he has the rest with the ace of diamonds and the last trump.

The "normal" heart play of taking a top heart before ruffing will put West in overruff position and result in the loss of a trump and a diamond. The correct play guarantees the slam as long as no suit breaks very badly.

The reason you need good-natured friends for this hand is that nobody likes to fail on a test.

Either Side May Use Golden Rule

Boy Scouts are sometimes considered models of good conduct, but a bridge expert can give an Eagle Scout cards and spades. The secret is the bridge player's Golden Rule: Do unto others as others do unto you—but beat them to it.

South dealer   **Both sides vulnerable**

NORTH
- ♠ 9 5 3 2
- ♡ K 7 3
- ◇ K Q J 6 5
- ♣ A

WEST   EAST
- ♠ 8   ♠ K Q J 10 6 4
- ♡ 10 9 4   ♡ A 8
- ◇ 10 8 7 2   ◇ A
- ♣ 9 8 5 4 2   ♣ 10 7 6 3

SOUTH-D
- ♠ A 7
- ♡ Q J 6 5 2
- ◇ 9 4 3
- ♣ K Q J

Defense Tricks:

☐ ☐ ☐ ☐ ☐ ☐ ☐ ☐ ☐ ☐ ☐ ☐ ☐

Bid the hand your way:

North	East	South	West
_____	_____	_____	_____
_____	_____	_____	_____
_____	_____	_____	_____
		Opening Lead _____	

How the hand was bid:

SOUTH	WEST	NORTH	EAST
1 ♡	Pass	2 ◇	2 ♠
Pass	Pass	3 ♡	Pass
4 ♡	All Pass		

Opening lead — ♠ 8

How the hand was played: South, no expert, took the ace of spades and led a trump, losing dummy's king to the ace. East cashed a high spade and led another high spade, putting South's trumps in the middle.

If South ruffed low, West would overruff; and if South ruffed with an honor, West would eventually get a trick with the ten of hearts.

South should lead a club to dummy's ace at the second trick and then lead a low trump from dummy. This maneuver puts East's trumps in the middle. If East steps up with the ace of trumps, collecting only low trumps, and leads high spades, South can afford to ruff with the jack. South can then draw trumps with the queen and king.

GETS WEST

If East plays low on the first round of trumps, South wins with the jack. He gets West by cashing the high clubs to discard two low spades from dummy. It is then safe to drive out the ace of trumps with the queen.

If East leads spades, South can ruff the third spade, putting West in the middle. If West overruffs, dummy is now ready to win by overruffing with the king of trumps.

Of course, East can prevent all this by applying the Golden Rule: He should get his own ruffing trick first. East takes the first trump with the ace, cashes the ace of diamonds and leads a low spade to force West to ruff. West returns a diamond, and East's ruff defeats the contract.

That Golden Rule works from any position at the table.

Don't Sell Brick to Wrong Customer

According to the latest guidebooks you can't sell a gold brick to a Hottentot. You have to find a customer who knows the value gold. The same principle applies to the kind of brick you have for sale during a game of bridge.

South dealer   **Both sides vulnerable**

```
                    NORTH
                ♠ K J 10 6
                ♡ A 3
                ◊ J 7 5 2
                ♣ 7 6 4

   WEST                        EAST
 ♠ A 9 3                      ♠ Q 8 7 4
 ♡ Q J 9 7 4                  ♡ K 10 6 5 2
 ◊ 6                          ◊ 8 4
 ♣ 9 8 5 2                    ♣ 10 3

                    SOUTH-D
                ♠ 5 2
                ♡ 8
                ◊ A K Q 10 9 3
                ♣ A K Q J
```

Defense Tricks:

☐ ☐ ☐ ☐ ☐ ☐ ☐ ☐ ☐ ☐ ☐ ☐ ☐

Bid the hand your way:

North	East	South	West
_____	_____	_____	_____
_____	_____	_____	_____
_____	_____	_____	_____
_____	_____	_____	_____

Opening Lead _____

26

How the hand was bid:

SOUTH	WEST	NORTH	EAST
2 ◊	Pass	3 ◊	Pass
4 NT	Pass	5 ◊	Pass
6 ◊	All Pass		

Opening lead — ♡ Q

How the hand was played: Declarer won the first trick in dummy with the ace of hearts and noticed that sooner or later he would have to lead a spade from his hand and guess whether to play the jack or the king from dummy.

Then South realized that West was a gold fancier. Perhaps he would be in the market for a nice brick.

South drew two rounds of trumps with the ace and king and then led a third trump to make sure West knew all about the trumps. South then ran the four clubs to make an important discard from the dummy.

Do you mean to say that you can't see any important discard in the dummy? It's easy to see that you've never sold gold bricks.

FALSE COUNT

South discarded the three of hearts from dummy. This would be useful only if South had a second heart—and this is just what South wanted West to believe. West already knew about South's six diamonds and four clubs, and if West thought that South had two hearts he would "know" that South had room in his hand for only one spade.

South waited for a few seconds to make sure that West had time to do his counting. Then South led a spade toward dummy.

West stepped right up with the ace of spades to make sure that South didn't put the ace to sleep with his "singleton" spade. West had bought the brick, and South didn't have to guess the right spade play from the dummy.

Bell Will Toll for Players

This would be a noisy world to live in if a bell rang every time we made a mistake. Most of us would have to wear earmuffs permanently, especially at the bridge table. For example, the bell would toll in the hand shown below.

North dealer   **Both sides vulnerable**

NORTH-D
♠ A J 10 9 7 6
♡ K 10 2
◊ 7 6 2
♣ 4

WEST

♠ 4 2
♡ 8 6 5
◊ K Q 9
♣ Q 10 8 3 2

EAST

♠ 3
♡ A J 9 4
◊ J 8 3
♣ K J 9 7 5

SOUTH
♠ K Q 8 5
♡ Q 7 3
◊ A 10 5 4
♣ A 6

Defense Tricks:

☐ ☐ ☐ ☐ ☐ ☐ ☐ ☐ ☐ ☐ ☐ ☐ ☐

Bid the hand your way:

North	East	South	West
_____	_____	_____	_____
_____	_____	_____	_____
_____	_____	_____	_____
_____	_____	_____	_____

Opening Lead _____

How the hand was bid:

NORTH	EAST	SOUTH	WEST
Pass	Pass	1 ♠	Pass
4 ♠	All Pass		

Opening lead — ♣ 3

How the hand was played: South won the first trick with the ace of clubs, drew two rounds of trumps and led a low diamond.

West won the nine of diamonds and led the eight of hearts through dummy. Declarer put up dummy's ten and won with the queen when East played the jack.

South continued with the ace of diamonds and a low diamond, losing again to West. Back came another heart, and East took two heart tricks to defeat the contract.

Did you hear the bell ring? Who made the mistake—and when?

EARLY MISTAKE

The bell rang for South when he played the ace of clubs at the first trick. The correct play is to let East win the first trick.

East returns a diamond, and South puts up the ace and cashes the ace of clubs to discard a diamond from dummy. Then South gives up a diamond.

West can lead just one heart through dummy. South wins with the queen of hearts, ruffs a diamond in dummy and draws trumps with the ace and king. His last diamond is good, so he discards a heart from dummy on it, thus losing only one club, one diamond and one heart instead of two diamonds and two hearts.

Declarer Overcomes Opposition

Authorities differ on the value of the dirty laugh at the bridge table. A coarse cackle may crack a timid player's morale, but will only inspire a courageous player to outdo himself. This may explain how South managed to make his slam in the following hand.

North dealer   **North-South vulnerable**

NORTH-D
♠ Q 5 4
♡ A 4
◇ A 8 7 4
♣ A 9 5 3

WEST	EAST
♠ K 10 8 6	♠ None
♡ J 7 6	♡ 10 9 5 3 2
◇ 10 6 3 2	◇ J 9 5
♣ J 4	♣ 10 8 7 6 2

SOUTH
♠ A J 9 7 3 2
♡ K Q 8
◇ K Q
♣ K Q

Defense Tricks:

☐ ☐ ☐ ☐ ☐ ☐ ☐ ☐ ☐ ☐ ☐ ☐ ☐ ☐

Bid the hand your way:

North	East	South	West
_____	_____	_____	_____
_____	_____	_____	_____
_____	_____	_____	_____
_____	_____	_____	_____
		Opening Lead _____	

30

How the hand was bid:

NORTH	EAST	SOUTH	WEST
1 ♣	Pass	2 ♠	Pass
3 ♠	Pass	4 NT	Pass
5 ♠	Pass	5 NT	Pass
6 ♣	Pass	6 ♠	All Pass

Opening lead — ♢ 2

How the hand was played: South won the opening diamond lead with the queen and led out the ace of spades, intending to give up one trump trick and claim the rest. When East discarded a club on the ace of spades South looked crest-fallen, and West thought the time had come for a triumphant snicker.

It was a poor idea, for South gritted his teeth and proceeded to make the contract. You might enjoy looking for the winning line of play before you read on.

OVERTAKING PLAYS

South led the king of diamonds and overtook with dummy's ace. Then he ruffed a diamond in his hand. He led a heart to the ace and ruffed dummy's last diamond. Then South took his high hearts, cashed the king of clubs and overtook the queen of clubs with dummy's ace.

At this stage, West and South each had three trumps left. Dummy had the lead, holding two trumps and a low club. Declarer led the club from dummy and played the jack of trumps from his hand.

If West played a low trump, South would lead a trump toward dummy's queen to make sure of the twelfth trick. West therefore overruffed with the king of trumps; but then he had to lead one of his two remaining trumps. If West led the ten of trumps, dummy would win with the queen and South would later win with the nine; and if West led the eight of trumps, South would let it ride around to the nine then and there. Either way, South was sure to make his slam.

Wandering Dummy Shows Bad Form

It's considered bad form to look at your partner's hand when you're going to be dummy, and it's even worse to get up and stand behind him to watch the way he butchers the hand. The ideal dummy sits still and smiles.

East dealer   **Neither side vulnerable**

NORTH
- ♠ Q J 10
- ♡ 8 5
- ◇ K 3
- ♣ A J 10 9 8 6

WEST
- ♠ 8 7
- ♡ 10 6 4 3 2
- ◇ Q 9 5
- ♣ 5 4 2

EAST-D
- ♠ K 9 6 3 2
- ♡ Q J 7
- ◇ A 10
- ♣ Q 7 3

SOUTH
- ♠ A 5 4
- ♡ A K 9
- ◇ J 8 7 6 4 2
- ♣ K

Defense Tricks:

☐ ☐ ☐ ☐ ☐ ☐ ☐ ☐ ☐ ☐ ☐ ☐ ☐

Bid the hand your way:

North	East	South	West
_____	_____	_____	_____
_____	_____	_____	_____
_____	_____	_____	_____
_____	_____	_____	_____
		Opening Lead	_____

How the hand was bid:

EAST	SOUTH	WEST	NORTH
1 ♠	Pass	Pass	2 ♣
Pass	3 NT	All Pass	

Opening lead — ♠ 8

How the hand was played: When this hand was played, North looked at his partner's hand before the opening lead was made. The look did him no good, for declarer allowed dummy's queen of spades to win the first trick.

North gurgled unhappily as declarer next led a low club to the king. South tried a diamond, losing the king to East's ace.

East returned the queen of hearts as a safe way of getting out. South won with the king of hearts and led a low diamond, hoping to drop the queen.

There was no such luck. East won with the ten of diamonds and led the jack of hearts. The defenders easily got three hearts and three diamonds, and South was down two.

ASKS QUESTION

North regained his smile, but South remembered the gurgle. "Could I have done better?" South asked.

"Yes," North assured him smoothly. "If you had seen all of the cards, you could have gone down three."

Declarer should win the first trick with the ace of spades even though East refuses to cover dummy's queen. South should then lead the king of clubs and overtake with dummy's ace. This puts him in position to continue with high clubs until East takes the queen.

South can get to dummy for the rest of the clubs by leading low spades. East can capture dummy's jack, but he cannot prevent the ten of spades from being an entry to the dummy. South wins at least two spades, two hearts and five clubs.

Historic Murder Traced to Bridge

The old records say that the trouble started when Abel traded a spade for two of Cain's clubs, and the older historians assumed this referred to a gardener's tool and a hunter's weapons. Actually, it was a bridge quarrel, and this book is scooping the whole world by bringing you the original hand.

South dealer   **North-South vulnerable**

NORTH
♠ A 3 2
♡ Q 6 5 3 2
♢ A K
♣ 8 4 3

WEST
♠ 7 5
♡ J 10 9
♢ 9 7 4 3 2
♣ K 10 2

EAST
♠ 9 8 6
♡ K 8 7 4
♢ 8 5
♣ Q 9 7 6

SOUTH-D
♠ K Q J 10 4
♡ A
♢ Q J 10 6
♣ A J 5

Defense Tricks:

☐ ☐ ☐ ☐ ☐ ☐ ☐ ☐ ☐ ☐ ☐ ☐ ☐ ☐

Bid the hand your way:

North	East	South	West
_____	_____	_____	_____
_____	_____	_____	_____
_____	_____	_____	_____
_____	_____	_____	_____
		Opening Lead	_____

34

How the hand was bid:

SOUTH	WEST	NORTH	EAST
1 ♠	Pass	2 ♡	Pass
3 ◇	Pass	4 ♠	Pass
6 ♠	All Pass		

Opening lead — ♡ J

How the hand was played: Abel won the first trick with the ace of hearts, drew two rounds of trumps with the king and ace and ruffed a low heart. He got back to dummy with the king of diamonds and ruffed another low heart.

The king of hearts did not fall, and Abel was tempted to draw the last trump and enter dummy with the ace of diamonds to lead a club. But then he would lose two club tricks, and history's earliest slam would have been defeated.

Just in time, Abel saw a better line of play. He did not draw the last trump. Instead, he led a diamond to dummy's ace and ruffed out the king of hearts. This set up dummy's last heart, but used up declarer's last trump.

CASHES DIAMONDS

Abel then led the queen of diamonds and discarded a club from dummy. Cain had a problem with the East hand. If Cain ruffed with the nine of spades, declarer would win the club return and cash the jack of diamonds to discard the last club from dummy.

Cain decided not to ruff the queen or jack of diamonds, but it did him no good. Abel discarded two clubs from dummy, cashed the ace of clubs and ruffed a club in dummy. Twelve tricks were in, and Cain could get only his last card—the high spade.

"Ha ha!" Abel laughed. "You thought you were going to get two clubs, but all you got was one spade."

That's where the story ends, but there are blood stains on the parchment.

Good Bridge Player Counts Trumps

"These modern bridge players can't even count trumps," the Old Kibitzer snorted. "It's that rock and roll they listen to. They hear that beat, and they can count up only to four. A bridge player must count to thirteen."

South dealer   **Both sides vulnerable**

NORTH
♠ K 10 2
♡ K 6 4
◇ 8 7 4
♣ 6 5 3 2

WEST   **EAST**
♠ 9 6 4   ♠ 7 5
♡ Q J 10 9 5 2   ♡ A 8 7 3
◇ A J 10   ◇ 9 6 3 2
♣ A   ♣ Q 9 8

SOUTH-D
♠ A Q J 8 3
♡ None
◇ K Q 5
♣ K J 10 7 4

Defense Tricks:

☐ ☐ ☐ ☐ ☐ ☐ ☐ ☐ ☐ ☐ ☐ ☐ ☐

Bid the hand your way:

North	East	South	West
_____	_____	_____	_____
_____	_____	_____	_____
_____	_____	_____	_____
_____	_____	_____	_____
		Opening Lead _____	

How the hand was bid:

SOUTH	WEST	NORTH	EAST
1 ♠	2 ♡	2 ♠	3 ♡
4 ♠	All Pass		

Opening lead — ♡ Q

How the hand was played: The old gentleman had just watched South play today's hand. South ruffed the first heart, led a trump to dummy's ten and returned a club to try a finesse with the jack.

West won with the ace of clubs and returned another heart. South ruffed again and led the queen of trumps to dummy's king. Then he led another club from dummy to finesse with the ten.

West ruffed with the nine of spades, and the Old Kibitzer stalked away from the table. "Anybody who can't draw trumps shouldn't be allowed to play bridge in a good club," he muttered.

MAKES GAME

Unperturbed by the loss of his audience, South ruffed West's third heart lead and ran all of the clubs, discarding a diamond from dummy. Then he gave up the king of diamonds to the ace, winning the last two tricks with the queen of diamonds and dummy's last trump.

What do you think about these modern bridge players? Do you agree with the Old Kibitzer, or do you think that South played the hand correctly?

South would go down if he drew three rounds of trumps. That would take all of his own trumps as well as all of West's. When South finished with his clubs, West would take the last three tricks with the ace of diamonds and two hearts. South would get four clubs and five trumps, but he would not get a diamond trick.

A good player must count his tricks as well as the trumps.

Be Practical—Not Merely Simple

An expert is reluctant to make a simple play if he can work out something complicated. If anybody notices, he feels as though he's been caught taking his own sandwiches to a swanky night club.

North dealer   **Both sides vulnerable**

NORTH-D
♠ Q 8
♡ A Q J 6 4
◇ K 7 6 3
♣ K 2

WEST   EAST
♠ J 10 3   ♠ 9 5
♡ K 9 7 3 2   ♡ 10 8
◇ 5 4   ◇ Q J 10 8 2
♣ A 9 5   ♣ 10 7 6 4

SOUTH
♠ A K 7 6 4 2
♡ 5
◇ A 9
♣ Q J 8 3

Defense Tricks:

☐ ☐ ☐ ☐ ☐ ☐ ☐ ☐ ☐ ☐ ☐ ☐

Bid the hand your way:

North	East	South	West
___	___	___	___
___	___	___	___
___	___	___	___
___	___	___	___

Opening Lead _____

How the hand was bid:

NORTH	EAST	SOUTH	WEST
1 ♡	Pass	2 ♠	Pass
3 ◇	Pass	3 ♠	Pass
4 ♠	Pass	4 NT	Pass
5 ◇	Pass	6 ♠	All Pass

Opening lead — ◇ 5

How the hand was played: An expert would win with the ace of diamonds and would run five rounds of trumps, discarding low hearts and a low diamond from the dummy. Then he would start the clubs, hoping to catch somebody in a squeeze at the twelfth trick.

If you're a simple, practical soul just rely on being able to ruff the third round of clubs in the dummy.

By the way, where did you decide to win the first diamond trick? If you don't come up with the right answer you may be simple, but you're not so practical.

WRONG ANSWER

See what happens if you win the first trick with the ace of diamonds. Lead a club to the king, and return a club, losing to West's ace. West returns a diamond to dummy's king.

Cash the ace of hearts and ruff a heart. Now lead the low club and ruff with dummy's eight of spades. Draw a round of trumps with dummy's queen, and all you need is to get back to your hand to draw trumps.

But you can't get back. If you lead a third heart, East inserts the nine of spades to force out a high trump from your hand. West will eventually get a trump trick.

Now try the right answer. Win the first trick with the king of diamonds, lead the king of clubs and continue with another club to force out the ace. When a diamond comes back you're in your hand—just where you want to be to ruff the low club in dummy.

Do Homework Away from Table

In some situations you must make the right play without thinking. Do a little thinking away from the table so that you can recognize these situations in a flash and then you have a chance to come up with the right answer effectively.

South dealer   **Both sides vulnerable**

                              NORTH
                              ♠ A 10 5 3
                              ♡ A K J 3
                              ◇ 6
                              ♣ 9 8 6 2

        WEST   EAST
        ♠ 9 8 4 2   ♠ 6
        ♡ 7 5 4   ♡ Q 10 9 8
        ◇ Q 5 2   ◇ A 10 8 7 4
        ♣ A J 5   ♣ 10 7 4

                              SOUTH-D
                              ♠ K Q J 7
                              ♡ 6 2
                              ◇ K J 9 3
                              ♣ K Q 3

Defense Tricks:

☐ ☐ ☐ ☐ ☐ ☐ ☐ ☐ ☐ ☐ ☐ ☐ ☐ ☐

Bid the hand your way:

North	East	South	West
_____	_____	_____	_____
_____	_____	_____	_____
_____	_____	_____	_____
_____	_____	_____	_____
		Opening Lead	_____

40

How the hand was bid:

SOUTH	WEST	NORTH	EAST
1 ♠	Pass	3 ♠	Pass
4 ♠	All Pass		

Opening lead — ♠ 2

How the hand was played: When this hand was played in the 1959 World Championship, both the American and the Argentine team bid up to four spades and got a trump opening lead. Both declarers won the first trick in dummy and returned the singleton six of diamonds.

The Argentine East hadn't been thinking ahead. He hesitated, and it became clear to everybody at the table that he had the ace of diamonds and was wondering what to do.

After about one second East played the ace of diamonds with a resigned shrug of the shoulders.

NO PROBLEM

The American declarer could win a trick, later, with the king of diamonds and could ruff two diamonds in dummy.

At the other table, Leonard Harmon held the East cards for the American team. When the singleton was led from the dummy, Harmon played low smoothly.

South now had to guess whether to play the king or the jack. It's easy for us to see the winning play, but in the actual match South played the jack.

West won with the queen of diamonds and returned another trump. South never won a trick with the king of diamonds, and he went down one.

The secret of Harmon's success was that he had done his homework away from the bridge table. He had discovered that it doesn't pay to come up with the ace when a singleton is led through you. You sometimes lose your ace by playing low, but you gain far more often than you lose.

Contract Depends on Reaching Hand

It helps to know where the cards are, but it doesn't always help enough. Try making four hearts on the following hand—and allow yourself to look at the East-West cards. You'll find it difficult enough.

West dealer   **North-South vulnerable**

                          NORTH
                          ♠ J 9 7 6 3
                          ♡ 7 6 3
                          ◇ A K Q
                          ♣ A 10

WEST-D   EAST
♠ A K Q 10 8   ♠ 5
♡ 9 8 5 2   ♡ 4
◇ 7   ◇ 10 9 8 3 2
♣ 9 8 4   ♣ K J 7 6 3 2

                          SOUTH
                          ♠ 4 2
                          ♡ A K Q J 10
                          ◇ J 6 5 4
                          ♣ Q 5

Defense Tricks:

☐ ☐ ☐ ☐ ☐ ☐ ☐ ☐ ☐ ☐ ☐ ☐ ☐

Bid the hand your way:

North	East	South	West
_____	_____	_____	_____
_____	_____	_____	_____
_____	_____	_____	_____
_____	_____	_____	_____
		Opening Lead	_____

How the hand was bid:

WEST	NORTH	EAST	SOUTH
Pass	1 ♠	Pass	2 ♡
Pass	2 NT	Pass	4 ♡
All Pass			

Opening lead — ♠ K

How the hand was played: West opened the king of spades and continued with the queen of spades. East discarded the seven of clubs, thus revealing the spade position and giving South a good idea of who held the king of clubs.

West shrewdly continued with a low spade to shorten South's trumps. East ruffed, and South overruffed.

South led the ace of trumps, and East discarded a low club, completing his high-low in that suit. Now South was sure that East held the king of clubs. West would not have passed originally with his strong spades, four hearts and the king of clubs.

DANGER AHEAD

South saw danger ahead. If he drew the rest of the trumps, he could then safely cash dummy's three high diamonds. That would give him nine tricks—five trumps, three diamonds and one club. But how could he get back to his hand for the jack of diamonds?

See if you can work out this problem before you read on. When the hand was played, South got back to his hand.

South drew the rest of the trumps. When he led his last trump he discarded a club from dummy. Not the ten of clubs. No, no. South discarded dummy's ace of clubs!

Now declarer cashed dummy's top diamonds and got out of dummy with the ten of clubs. East could take the king of clubs, but had to return a club or a diamond. Either way South was sure to win tricks with the queen of clubs and the jack of diamonds.

Scientific Approach to Ailments

"We scientific men call it the death wish," I said in my best impressive tone. After all, what's the use of having a bridge clinic and putting on a white coat if you can't impress your patients?

South dealer   **Both sides vulnerable**

```
                        NORTH
                        ♠ J 10 4 3
                        ♡ 9 4
                        ◊ K 6 5 2
                        ♣ K 9 4
        WEST                            EAST
        ♠ A 7 5                         ♠ 6
        ♡ Q J 7 3                       ♡ 10 6 5
        ◊ J 10 9 4                      ◊ A Q 8 7
        ♣ 6 3                           ♣ Q J 10 8 2
                        SOUTH-D
                        ♠ K Q 9 8 2
                        ♡ A K 8 2
                        ◊ 3
                        ♣ A 7 5
```

Defense Tricks:

☐ ☐ ☐ ☐ ☐ ☐ ☐ ☐ ☐ ☐ ☐ ☐ ☐

Bid the hand your way:

North	East	South	West
_____	_____	_____	_____
_____	_____	_____	_____
_____	_____	_____	_____
_____	_____	_____	_____
		Opening Lead	_____

How the hand was bid:

SOUTH	WEST	NORTH	EAST
1 ♠	Pass	2 ♠	Pass
4 ♠	All Pass		

Opening lead — ◊ J

How the hand was played: "Now take this prescription to the nearest stationery store," I said, scribbling busily at my desk. "Give it to the owner. He won't be able to read it, so he'll ask you what you want. Tell him you want a big notebook."

"When you get the notebook home, write in it 'I must not draw trumps too soon' five hundred times a day. Stop the treatment when your pen runs out of ink."

The same prescription is offered free of charge to all readers. And the hand on the opposite page shows the sort of thing that brings many patients to me.

NEEDS RUFFS

South must ruff two low hearts in the dummy to make sure of his game contract. He will lose a diamond, a trump and a club. You wouldn't think you need a doctor for this sort of hand, but every doctor could tell you stories that would curl your hair.

South actually ruffed the second round of diamonds and led the king of spades. There was no harm in this, but the habit grew on South. He led another spade.

West took the ace of spades and led a third spade. This left only one trump in dummy, and South discovered that he couldn't ruff two hearts with only one trump.

South eventually lost one trick in each suit and came to my clinic doubled up with pain. (His partner was a violent type.) Now he has his notebook and you'd be surprised how his penmanship has improved. But he still draws trumps too soon.

Bridge Problem Stumps Friends

There's a right way and a wrong way to give a bridge problem to your friends. Be helpful, and you can count on getting the wrong answer.

South dealer   **Both sides vulnerable**

NORTH
- ♠ K Q J 5 3
- ♡ K J
- ♢ J 6 3 2
- ♣ 7 4

WEST
- ♠ 8 4
- ♡ 7 4
- ♢ A 10 9 8
- ♣ K J 8 5 3

EAST
- ♠ A 10 9 6
- ♡ 9 8 6 5 2
- ♢ 4
- ♣ 9 6 2

SOUTH-D
- ♠ 7 2
- ♡ A Q 10 3
- ♢ K Q 7 5
- ♣ A Q 10

Defense Tricks:

☐ ☐ ☐ ☐ ☐ ☐ ☐ ☐ ☐ ☐ ☐ ☐

Bid the hand your way:

North	East	South	West
_____	_____	_____	_____
_____	_____	_____	_____
_____	_____	_____	_____
_____	_____	_____	_____
		Opening Lead _____	

How the hand was bid:

SOUTH	WEST	NORTH	EAST
1 NT	Pass	3 ♠	Pass
3 NT	All Pass		

Opening lead — ♣ 5

How the hand was played: Show the North-South hands to a friend and tell him that he wins the first club trick with the ten. "You can surely win two clubs and four hearts," you tell him, "so you need three tricks in spades and diamonds combined." With the stage thus set you ask your question: "Which suit should South lead first?"

The average player says "Spades." The good player answers "Diamonds." In either case you smile and point out that South must lead a heart at the second trick.

MUST REACH DUMMY

South must reach the dummy to return a low diamond at the third trick. If East has the ace of diamonds and plays it, South can win three diamond tricks. If East has the ace of diamonds and fails to play it, South can win a diamond trick and then shifts to spades to make sure of two spade tricks.

If West has the ace of diamonds, he can win the first diamond trick but cannot safely continue the attack on clubs. South has time to develop two spade tricks.

It would be wrong to lead a diamond from the South hand because *East* might have A-10-9-8. If so, East would capture an honor with the ace of diamonds and would return a club. South would get only two diamond tricks and would go down if West had the ace of spades as an entry to the clubs.

It is wrong to lead spades first because East captures an honor with the ace and returns a club. West gets in with the ace of diamonds in time to run his clubs.

Diamonds is the suit to develop first, but South must begin with a heart to lead diamonds from the correct direction.

Useless Cards Have Their Uses

Nobody knows better than bridge players how hard it is to live a blameless life. It helps to know, however, that when you falter your friends will tell you all about it.

North dealer   **Both sides vulnerable**

NORTH-D
- ♠ 9 4
- ♡ A 10 7 6 3
- ◇ 10 6
- ♣ A 8 7 4

WEST
- ♠ 8 7 3
- ♡ 2
- ◇ K 8 7 2
- ♣ Q J 6 5 2

EAST
- ♠ A
- ♡ Q J 9 8 4
- ◇ A 5 4
- ♣ K 10 9 3

SOUTH
- ♠ K Q J 10 6 5 2
- ♡ K 5
- ◇ Q J 9 3
- ♣ None

Defense Tricks:

☐ ☐ ☐ ☐ ☐ ☐ ☐ ☐ ☐ ☐ ☐ ☐ ☐

Bid the hand your way:

North	East	South	West
_____	_____	_____	_____
_____	_____	_____	_____
_____	_____	_____	_____
		Opening Lead _____	

48

How the hand was bid:

NORTH	EAST	SOUTH	WEST
Pass	1 ♡	4 ♠	All Pass

Opening lead — ♡ 2

How the hand was played: South won the first trick with the king of hearts and craftily led the queen of spades from his West held the ace of spades, he might hold off the first trump trick for fear that East had the singleton king.

It was a good idea, but it came to nothing. East won with the ace of spades and returned the queen of hearts for his partner to ruff.

The defenders later got two diamond tricks, and South lost all save honors.

USELESS ACE

South noticed the gleam in his partner's eye and offered apologetically: "You had the wrong ace for me. That ace of clubs was useless."

"Not half as useless as certain partners," North observed. "Mind you, I name no names."

Maybe you can guess whom North had in mind. Do you also know why he was so annoyed? See if you can spot the right play before you read on.

Declarer should win the first trick in dummy with the ace of hearts. He should then cash the useless ace of clubs in order to get rid of the useless king of hearts!

Only then can declarer afford to lead a trump. The defenders get the ace of spades and two diamonds, but nothing else.

Desperate Play for Right Tricks

Since most bridge players lead a sheltered life, they don't know what it is to be desperate. Yet there are times when only a desperate play will develop the right number of tricks.

East dealer   **Neither side vulnerable**

```
                    NORTH
                    ♠ Q J 4
                    ♡ K Q 9
                    ◊ A 5 4
                    ♣ A K Q J
      WEST                         EAST-D
      ♠ A 10 8 3 2                 ♠ K 7 6 5
      ♡ 7                          ♡ A 5 3 2
      ◊ 9 8 7 3                    ◊ K 6 2
      ♣ 8 6 5                      ♣ 7 4
                    SOUTH
                    ♠ 9
                    ♡ J 10 8 6 4
                    ◊ Q J 10
                    ♣ 10 9 3 2
```

Defense Tricks:

☐ ☐ ☐ ☐ ☐ ☐ ☐ ☐ ☐ ☐ ☐ ☐

Bid the hand your way:

North	East	South	West
———	———	———	———
———	———	———	———
———	———	———	———
———	———		———

                           Opening Lead ———

How the hand was bid:

EAST	SOUTH	WEST	NORTH
Pass	Pass	Pass	2 NT
Pass	3 ♡	Pass	4 ♡
All Pass			

Opening lead — ◊ 9

How the hand was played: West opens the nine of diamonds, and declarer plays low from dummy. East wins with the king of diamonds and is then at the crossroads.

If East makes a normal good-mannered return, South makes the contract. For example, if East returns a diamond, dummy wins and leads trumps until East takes the ace.

South gets the lead with the queen of diamonds to draw the rest of the trumps, and then declarer easily takes ten tricks.

The hand can be defeated only if West has the ace of spades. One hope is to take two spade tricks immediately; another hope is to make declarer ruff enough spades to lose control of the trumps.

RIGHT CARD

East must lead the king of spades. This is desperate, to be sure, but quite safe if West has the ace of spades.

When the king of spades wins the trick, East continues with a low spade. South must ruff, and is thus reduced to four trumps. When East gets in with the ace of trumps he leads another spade, and South is forced to ruff again. This leaves East with one trump more than declarer, so that East gets the setting trick with a low trump.

East could not defeat the contract by leading a low spade at the second trick. West would take the ace and return a spade, whereupon declarer would ruff East's king. Then dummy's queen of spades would be good, so that East would be unable to make South ruff a second time.

Magnifying Glass May Detect Criminal

Students of crime will find something to interest them in the report of the following hand. It's easy to detect the criminal by guesswork alone, but spotting his crime is not nearly so easy.

South dealer   **Both sides vulnerable**

NORTH
♠ A 8 6
♡ A Q 5
◇ 7 6 4
♣ A Q J 9

WEST   EAST
♠ K Q 10 7 5 3   ♠ J 9 4
♡ 6   ♡ 9 3
◇ A Q 10   ◇ J 8 5 2
♣ 7 5 2   ♣ K 8 4 3

SOUTH-D
♠ 2
♡ K J 10 8 7 4 2
◇ K 9 3
♣ 10 6

Defense Tricks:

☐ ☐ ☐ ☐ ☐ ☐ ☐ ☐ ☐ ☐ ☐ ☐

Bid the hand your way:

North	East	South	West
_____	_____	_____	_____
_____	_____	_____	_____
_____	_____	_____	_____
		_____	_____

Opening Lead _____

How the hand was bid:

SOUTH	WEST	NORTH	EAST
3 ♡	3 ♠	4 ♡	All Pass

Opening lead — ♠ K

How the hand was played: West led the king of spades, and dummy's ace won. Declarer drew two rounds of trumps and then led the ten of clubs for a finesse. East won with the king of clubs and returned the deuce of diamonds.

South played the nine of diamonds, and West won with the ten. Now West had to take the ace of diamonds in a hurry since otherwise declarer would discard two diamonds on dummy's good clubs. The defenders got only two diamonds and one club, so South made his contract.

Of course you know the criminal and his crime—or do you? Decide for yourself before you read on; but take a second look to make sure you've seen all the skulduggery.

OBVIOUS CRIME

There was one obvious crime in the play of the cards. When East got the king of clubs, he should return the jack of diamonds instead of the deuce. Then West would get three diamond tricks, defeating the contract.

But if you've tucked away your magnifying glass, Sherlock, you'd better take up gin rummy. South was just as big a criminal as East. It was a crime to win the first trick.

The correct play is to refuse the first trick, take the second spade, discarding a club, and draw trumps with the king and queen. Then declarer cashes the ace of clubs and leads the queen of clubs for a ruffing finesse.

If East puts up the king of clubs, South ruffs and returns to dummy with a trump to discard two diamonds on good clubs. If East fails to put up the king of clubs. South throws a diamond and continues with the jack of clubs to make sure of another diamond discard.

Sure Thing Better Than Good Odds

It's quite reasonable to bid a slam that depends on a finesse, and better than reasonable if you need only one out of two finesses. Still, don't settle for this 3 to 1 shot if you can get even better odds.

South dealer   **Both sides vulnerable**

NORTH
- ♠ J 6 2
- ♡ A
- ◇ A J 7 6 3 2
- ♣ Q 6 3

WEST
- ♠ 10
- ♡ K 10 5 4
- ◇ K Q 10 9 8
- ♣ J 9 4

EAST
- ♠ 5 4
- ♡ J 9 8 7 3 2
- ◇ 4
- ♣ K 8 5 2

SOUTH-D
- ♠ A K Q 9 8 7 3
- ♡ Q 6
- ◇ 5
- ♣ A 10 7

Defense Tricks:

☐ ☐ ☐ ☐ ☐ ☐ ☐ ☐ ☐ ☐ ☐ ☐ ☐

Bid the hand your way:

North	East	South	West
____	____	____	____
____	____	____	____
____	____	____	____
____	____	____	____
		Opening Lead	____

How the hand was bid:

SOUTH	WEST	NORTH	EAST
1 ♠	Pass	2 ◊	Pass
4 ♠	Pass	5 ♡	Pass
6 ♠	All Pass		

Opening lead — ◊ K

How the hand was played: Declarer won the first trick in dummy with the ace of diamonds and drew two rounds of trumps. Then he led a low club toward dummy, losing the queen to East's king.

South still had the chance of another club finesse, but his ten lost to West's jack. Down one.

As South played the hand, the odds were 3 to 1 in his favor, but he overlooked a better chance. The correct play is to try to set up one of dummy's diamonds. If this fails to work, South can fall back on the clubs.

RUFF IMMEDIATELY

After winning the first trick with the ace of diamonds, South should immediately ruff a diamond with a high trump. He then leads the seven of spades to dummy's jack.

When the ten of spades falls on this trick, South is home. He ruffs another diamond with a high trump and leads the three of trumps to dummy's six. This permits him to ruff a third low diamond.

Declarer leads a heart to dummy's ace and ruffs a fourth low diamond. This clears the last diamond out of West's hand. South ruffs his queen of hearts with dummy's last trump and cashes dummy's jack of diamonds to discard a club.

When the diamonds broke 5-1, South needed a good trump break. If the ten of spades failed to drop, South could abandon the diamonds, draw a second trump and play for the clubs. It cost nothing to try first for the diamonds.

Thought Needed to Stop Long Suit

Even when you can win two tricks in a suit, it may still be important to refuse the first trick. This helps you when one of the opponents has only two cards in the dangerous suit.

North dealer   **North-South vulnerable**

NORTH-D

♠ Q J 4
♡ A 10 9
◇ J 7 4
♣ A K 9 5

WEST   **EAST**

♠ 6 3   ♠ K 10 9 8 5
♡ 7 5 4 3   ♡ K J 2
◇ A 6   ◇ K 8 3 2
♣ 8 6 4 3 2   ♣ 10

SOUTH

♠ A 7 2
♡ Q 8 6
◇ Q 10 9 5
♣ Q J 7

Defense Tricks:

☐ ☐ ☐ ☐ ☐ ☐ ☐ ☐ ☐ ☐ ☐ ☐ ☐

Bid the hand your way:

North	East	South	West
_____	_____	_____	_____
_____	_____	_____	_____
_____	_____	_____	_____
		Opening Lead _____	

56

How the hand was bid:

NORTH	EAST	SOUTH	WEST
1 ♣	1 ♠	1 NT	Pass
3 NT	All Pass		

Opening lead — ♠ 6

How the hand was played: You lose game and rubber if you play the queen or jack of spades from dummy at the first trick. If you've already mentally played the queen, give yourself a mental slap on the wrist and play the hand over.

If you play dummy's queen, East must not cover with the king. Instead, he signals encouragingly with the ten of spades.

Since you need at least one diamond trick, you lead a diamond at an early stage, and West takes the ace. He leads his other spade through dummy's J-4, and East can use either the king or the eight, depending on dummy's play. Either way, East sets up the rest of his spades.

East gets in with the king of diamonds in time to defeat the contract with the rest of the spades.

PLAY LOW

The correct procedure is to play low from both hands at the first trick. This allows East to win the first trick with the eight of spades, but nothing can stop you from taking the second and third spade tricks by way of a finesse.

If East returns a spade (as good a defense as any), you win in dummy with the jack and lead a diamond. If West wins, he cannot lead a spade, and you have time to force out the king of diamonds. If East wins the first diamond, he can set up his spades but cannot get back to cash them.

What happens if West takes the first diamond and leads a heart? Step up with the ace of hearts and lead another diamond. The opponents can take only two diamonds, one heart and one spade.

Good Player Sees through Cards

"There's something very suspicious about one of our bridge players," writes a Louisville fan. "I'm inclined to think he sees more than he ought to."

South dealer   **Both sides vulnerable**

NORTH
♠ A 10 9 8
♡ 7 4 2
◇ 6 5 3
♣ Q 5 4

WEST	EAST
♠ 5 3	♠ 4 2
♡ A K J 9 8	♡ 10 6 5 3
◇ A 9 8 7	◇ Q J 10
♣ 6 3	♣ J 9 8 7

SOUTH-D
♠ K Q J 7 6
♡ Q
◇ K 4 2
♣ A K 10 2

Defense Tricks:

☐ ☐ ☐ ☐ ☐ ☐ ☐ ☐ ☐ ☐ ☐ ☐

Bid the hand your way:

North	East	South	West
___	___	___	___
___	___	___	___
___	___	___	___
___	___	___	___
		Opening Lead ___	

58

How the hand was bid:

SOUTH	WEST	NORTH	EAST
1 ♠	2 ♡	2 ♠	Pass
4 ♠	All Pass		

Opening lead — ♡ K

How the hand was played: "He ruffed the second heart in the closed hand, drew trumps with the king and ace and ruffed dummy's last heart.

"Then he took the ace and queen of clubs. When he led dummy's last club my partner played the nine with never a trace of hesitation. Still, declarer finessed with the ten of clubs without any problem—just as though he had seen the jack in my partner's hand.

"What should I do about this?"

CONGRATULATE OPPONENT

Congratulate your opponent instead of suspecting him. It's always possible that an opponent will spot a card by good eyesight, but good play is a far more likely explanation.

When South took the club finesse, he was sure of his contract no matter who had the jack of clubs. If West had the jack, he could take the club but would then have to lead diamonds or hearts. Either way, South would lose only one diamond trick.

If South played the three top clubs, he would lose the contract since he would eventually lose three diamond tricks.

The tip-off is South's care in ruffing dummy's last heart. This set the stage for the eventual club finesse to guarantee the contract.

Unlucky Player Finds Sympathy

"I'm the unluckiest bridge player in the world," one of my friends announced the other day. And he shoved a bridge hand under my nose.

North dealer   **Both sides vulnerable**

NORTH-D
♠ Q J 7 2
♡ A K Q
♢ A K
♣ J 6 4 3

WEST   **EAST**
♠ 9 8 6 5 4   ♠ None
♡ 10 8   ♡ J 6 5 4 3
♢ J 10 9 8   ♢ 7 6 5 3
♣ K 5   ♣ A Q 10 9

SOUTH
♠ A K 10 3
♡ 9 7 2
♢ Q 4 2
♣ 8 7 2

Defense Tricks:

☐ ☐ ☐ ☐ ☐ ☐ ☐ ☐ ☐ ☐ ☐ ☐ ☐

Bid the hand your way:

North	East	South	West
____	____	____	____
____	____	____	____
____	____	____	____
____	____	____	____

Opening Lead _____

How the hand was bid:

NORTH	EAST	SOUTH	WEST
1 ♣	Pass	1 ♠	Pass
4 ♠	All Pass		

Opening lead — ◊ J

How the hand was played: "Wouldn't it burn you up to get to four spades and then find all the trumps in one hand?" he demanded.

"I got four trump tricks, three diamonds but only two hearts," he ended. And he looked almost happy to be so unlucky.

Now everybody knows that a bridge writer is the tenderest of God's creatures, but there is a limit to our sweeetness. "You'll find sympathy in the dictionary between Stupid and Throw-off," I informed my friend. And I refused to say another word until he had paid for my lunch.

CLUE SHOULD HELP

No reader of this book would be stuck for the lunch tab, especially with that clue about the location of sympathy.

South can make his contract if he throws off properly. There is no need to rely on West to hold three hearts.

Declarer wins the first trick in dummy with the king of diamonds and leads a trump to the ace, discovering the bad news. Time out for a groan or two.

Then South cashes two—and only two—of dummy's high hearts. He continues with the ace of diamonds and a trump to the king. Then he leads the queen of diamonds and discards dummy's ace of hearts!

Declarer is now in position to ruff a heart in dummy with the jack of spades. Eight tricks are home, and South still has dummy's queen of spades and his own ten to win the ninth and tenth tricks.

Automatic Return May Not Be Best

In the old days there were two sure ways to recognize a gentleman: he always stood up when a lady entered the room, and he always returned his partner's suit. Today a gentleman stands up for a lady mostly in self-defense and returns his partner's suit only when it pleases him to do so.

South dealer　　　　　　　　　　**Both sides vulnerable**

NORTH
- ♠ 10 8 4
- ♡ J 5 3
- ◇ K J 9 6
- ♣ K 10 2

WEST
- ♠ J 7 5 2
- ♡ K 9 4
- ◇ 7 4
- ♣ 9 7 6 5

EAST
- ♠ A 6
- ♡ A 8 7 6 2
- ◇ Q 10 5
- ♣ 8 4 3

SOUTH-D
- ♠ K Q 9 3
- ♡ Q 10
- ◇ A 8 3 2
- ♣ A Q J

Defense Tricks:

☐ ☐ ☐ ☐ ☐ ☐ ☐ ☐ ☐ ☐ ☐ ☐

Bid the hand your way:

North	East	South	West
_____	_____	_____	_____
_____	_____	_____	_____
_____	_____	_____	_____
_____	_____	_____	_____
		Opening Lead	_____

How the hand was bid:

SOUTH	WEST	NORTH	EAST
1 NT	Pass	2 NT	Pass
3 NT	All Pass		

Opening lead — ♠ 2

How the hand was played: Take the situation in this hand. East wins the first trick with the ace of spades and, being an old-fashioned gentleman, returns his other spade.

South wins with the king of spades and develops the diamonds, losing a trick to East in the process. East's return no longer matters, since South is sure to make the contract.

Declarer is sure to win two spades, three diamonds and three clubs. He can develop a heart as his ninth trick, and the opponents can do nothing about it.

TIMELY SWITCH

East can defeat the contract by switching to hearts after winning the first trick. West's lead of the deuce of spades shows that he has only four spades, which means that South also has four spades. There cannot be much nourishment in such a suit, but hearts may be the stuff to feed the troops.

West wins the second trick with the king of hearts and returns a heart. East gains the lead with a diamond in time to defeat the contract with the rest of the hearts.

Note that West does return his partner's suit—hearts. It is clear that East has rejected spades, presumably for a good reason. West has no reason to reject hearts, so he returns the suit. This, essentially, is the modern rule: Return your partner's suit unless you have a good reason to switch.

Get the Bloodhounds for Criminal

This is the time of year to give your dogs a good workout. Give them a deck of cards to sniff and see if they track down the criminal in the following hand.

South dealer   **North-South vulnerable**

```
                        NORTH
                        ♠ A 4 2
                        ♡ Q 5 4 2
                        ◇ 9 6 5 3
                        ♣ 6 2

        WEST                            EAST
        ♠ 8 5 3                         ♠ 7
        ♡ J 10 9                        ♡ K 8 7 3
        ◇ J 8 7 2                       ◇ Q 10 4
        ♣ A J 7                         ♣ Q 10 9 8 4

                        SOUTH-D
                        ♠ K Q J 10 9 6
                        ♡ A 6
                        ◇ A K
                        ♣ K 5 3
```

Defense Tricks:

☐ ☐ ☐ ☐ ☐ ☐ ☐ ☐ ☐ ☐ ☐ ☐ ☐

Bid the hand your way:

North	East	South	West
_____	_____	_____	_____
_____	_____	_____	_____
_____	_____	_____	_____
_____	_____	_____	_____
		Opening Lead _____	

How the hand was bid:

SOUTH	WEST	NORTH	EAST
1 ♠	Pass	2 ♠	Pass
4 ♠	All Pass		

Opening lead — ♡ J

How the hand was played: West opened the jack of hearts, declarer played the queen from dummy and East covered with the king. South won with the ace of hearts, led a spade to dummy's ace and returned a club, losing the king to West's ace of clubs.

West returned a trump, stepped up with the jack of clubs at the next trick and returned another trump to take the last trump out of dummy. South eventually lost a third club trick but broke even because of his 100 honors.

Don't let your dogs chew up everybody at the table. At least one player was innocent of all wrongdoing.

SURE THING

South was the chief criminal, for he had a sure thing after the heart opening lead. South should lead a low club from his hand at the second trick.

If the opponents return a trump, South wins and leads a second club. If they again return a trump, South wins and leads his last club to ruff with dummy's ace of spades. Then South can get back with a high diamond to draw the last trump. He loses only one heart and two clubs.

You can't really call West a criminal for his opening lead, but you might let your favorite dog take one bite. If West opens a trump, he can stop South from ruffing a club in dummy. It's hard for West to know that he must lead a trump at each opportunity, but he does have strength in each side suit, so the trump lead is indicated.

North and East get off scot free. Even a bridge player is sometimes innocent.

What Can Be Surer Than Finesses?

In a well-behaved bridge hand you can expect a finesse to suc-
ceed about half of the time. If you have two finesses, the odds
are 3 to 1 that at least one of them will work. The trouble is that
even long shots sometimes come in; you sometimes have a hand
in which no finesse works.

South dealer   **North-South vulnerable**

NORTH
- ♠ Q J 6
- ♡ K 8 7 3
- ◇ K 8 5
- ♣ A 6 3

WEST
- ♠ K 7 5 2
- ♡ A 6 4
- ◇ Q J 10 6
- ♣ 9 7

EAST
- ♠ 9 8 4 3
- ♡ 5
- ◇ 9 4 3
- ♣ K 8 5 4 2

SOUTH-D
- ♠ A 10
- ♡ Q J 10 9 2
- ◇ A 7 2
- ♣ Q J 10

Defense Tricks:

☐ ☐ ☐ ☐ ☐ ☐ ☐ ☐ ☐ ☐ ☐ ☐ ☐

Bid the hand your way:

North	East	South	West
———	———	———	———
———	———	———	———
———	———	———	———
———	———	———	———
		Opening Lead ———	

How the hand was bid:

SOUTH	WEST	NORTH	EAST
1 ♡	Pass	3 ♡	Pass
4 ♡	All Pass		

Opening lead — ◊ Q

How the hand was played: West opened the queen of diamonds, and South was as happy as a dog with two dinners as he looked at the dummy. He had a finesse in each black suit, and the contract was safe if either finesse worked.

South took the first diamond with the ace and led a trump. West grabbed the ace of hearts on the run and returned the jack of diamonds to knock out dummy's king.

"You'll sprain your wrist playing so fast," South chided him airily. And declarer drew two more rounds of trumps.

South next tried the spade finesse, losing to the king. West happily cashed a diamond trick, and now the contract depended on the club finesse.

FIRST TWINGE

South felt his first twinge when he tested the clubs; East looked too happy. Sure enough, East turned up with the king of clubs, and South had lost a trick in each suit. Down one.

South made his mistake when he looked at the dummy and assumed that a finesse was going to work. Correct play assures the contract regardless of the finesses.

Declarer should win the first diamond with the ace, cash the ace of spades and then give up a spade trick. He wins the diamond return with dummy's king and cashes the queen of spades to get rid of a diamond.

Having disposed of his diamond loser, South can afford to lose a spade, a trump and a club.

Break Rules for Beginners

A beginner should play low in second position, just as a child should stay on the sidewalk. In time, both the bridge beginner and the child learn when to break these rules.

North dealer   **North-South vulnerable**

NORTH-D

♠ 5 3 2
♡ A K Q 3
◇ A K 7 5
♣ 7 4

WEST	EAST
♠ 7 4	♠ K Q J 10 9
♡ J 10 9 7 6	♡ 8 2
◇ Q J 10	◇ 9 8 6 2
♣ J 9 8	♣ K 5

SOUTH

♠ A 8 6
♡ 5 4
◇ 4 3
♣ A Q 10 6 3 2

Defense Tricks:

☐ ☐ ☐ ☐ ☐ ☐ ☐ ☐ ☐ ☐ ☐ ☐

Bid the hand your way:

North	East	South	West
_____	_____	_____	_____
_____	_____	_____	_____
_____	_____	_____	_____
_____	_____	_____	_____

Opening Lead _____

How the hand was bid:

NORTH	EAST	SOUTH	WEST
1 ♡	1 ♠	2 ♣	Pass
2 ◊	Pass	2 NT	Pass
3 NT	All Pass		

Opening lead — ♠ 7

How the hand was played: South refused the first spade but won the second and led a heart to dummy. Then he returned a club from dummy, and East followed the rule for beginners by playing his low club.

Declarer finessed with the ten of clubs, and West won with the jack. It didn't matter what West returned, for South's clubs were about to produce five tricks. Declarer thus wound up with a total of eleven tricks.

Now go back to the fourth trick and see what happens if East puts up the king, as he should. South cannot refuse the trick, since then East would defeat the contract with the rest of the spades.

CANNOT RUN SUIT

When South wins the first club trick, he can no longer run the suit. West still has a club stopper, and South has no side entry to the clubs.

South can bring in only two club tricks and can thus win only eight tricks by normal play. At the table, South would probably return to dummy with a heart or diamond and lead a club to try a finesse with the ten. This play would be as helpful as a broken leg, for South might go down two instead of one.

If South tries an abnormal play, he can still make the contract after the first club trick. He cashes dummy's high hearts and diamonds and then leads any red card to throw West into the lead. West can take three tricks but must then lead a club, giving South two more club tricks and his contract.

Remember Combination in All Its Forms

It pays to remember certain combinations of cards no matter how they happen to be disguised. Your memory will pay off every now and then with the trick that brings in the game and rubber.

South dealer   **Both sides vulnerable**

NORTH
- ♠ 10 5 3
- ♡ 9 6
- ◊ A K 9 5 3
- ♣ K J 5

WEST
- ♠ A Q
- ♡ Q 10 8 4 3
- ◊ Q 10 8 6
- ♣ 4 2

EAST
- ♠ J 9 8 4
- ♡ J 7 2
- ◊ 7
- ♣ 10 9 7 6 3

SOUTH-D
- ♠ K 7 6 2
- ♡ A K 5
- ◊ J 4 2
- ♣ A Q 8

Defense Tricks:

☐ ☐ ☐ ☐ ☐ ☐ ☐ ☐ ☐ ☐ ☐ ☐

Bid the hand your way:

North	East	South	West
_____	_____	_____	_____
_____	_____	_____	_____
_____	_____	_____	_____
_____	_____	_____	_____

Opening Lead _____

How the hand was bid:

SOUTH	WEST	NORTH	EAST
1 NT	Pass	3 NT	All Pass

Opening lead — ♡ 4

How the hand was played: The combination in this case is in the diamond suit. Play it correctly and you get four diamond tricks. Careless play will develop only three tricks.

Win the first heart with the king, lead a diamond to dummy's king and then make the key play. Return a low diamond from dummy.

When East discards a club, you put up the jack of diamonds to force out West's queen. Later you can lead your last diamond to finesse through West's 10-8, since dummy has A-9-5 behind West.

If you carelessly led out the ace and king of diamonds, West would have two sure diamond tricks. You would have a hard time developing eight tricks, let alone nine.

LEAD TOWARD JACK

Sometimes you see this combination with the ace and king in separate hands. For example, you might have A-J-2 in your own hand, with K-9-5-4-3 in the dummy. Cash the ace first, get to dummy with a side suit and then lead low from the dummy toward your jack.

Another possibility is K-J-2 in your hand, with A-9-5-4-3 in dummy. Cash the king, get to dummy with a side suit and lead low from dummy toward the jack.

This play guards you against Q-10-x-x in either opponent's hand. We have seen what happens if West has the four diamonds. If East has them, he can take the queen when the low card is led from dummy; otherwise, South will win with the jack. East can get only his queen, then or later.

Prepare Handcuffs for Criminal

If you're a good bridge detective, you keep a pair of handcuffs in your pocket. You never know when you're going to need them. At the right moment you want to get up from your chair and snap them on some bridge criminal's wrists.

South dealer   **North-South vulnerable**

NORTH
- ♠ A J 10
- ♡ 5 2
- ♢ A 9 8 7 2
- ♣ A J 9

WEST
- ♠ 8 5 2
- ♡ 6 3
- ♢ K Q 4 3
- ♣ 6 5 4 2

EAST
- ♠ 7 6 4 3
- ♡ A K Q 10 4
- ♢ 6
- ♣ 8 7 3

SOUTH-D
- ♠ K Q 9
- ♡ J 9 8 7
- ♢ J 10 5
- ♣ K Q 10

Defense Tricks:

☐ ☐ ☐ ☐ ☐ ☐ ☐ ☐ ☐ ☐ ☐ ☐ ☐

Bid the hand your way:

North	East	South	West
_____	_____	_____	_____
_____	_____	_____	_____
_____	_____	_____	_____
_____	_____	_____	_____
		Opening Lead _____	

How the hand was bid:

SOUTH	WEST	NORTH	EAST
Pass	Pass	1 ◇	1 ♡
2 NT	Pass	3 NT	All Pass

Opening lead — ♡ 6

How the hand was played: Imagine you're watching the play of this hand. Keep the handcuffs ready and watch for the criminal to show himself.

West opens the six of hearts, and East takes the queen, king and ace of hearts in that order. South wins the fourth heart trick and leads the jack of diamonds.

West covers with the queen of diamonds, and dummy wins with the ace. Back comes a diamond to the king. South then claims the rest of the tricks, making game and rubber.

You're slow, Hawkshaw! You should have slipped the bracelets on the criminal and should be marching him off to the stationhouse by now.

BLACK CRIME

It's a black crime, and East is the criminal. His very first play was the crime.

West has opened the six of hearts, his top card in East's suit. This means that South has the missing higher hearts—J-9-8-7. If East wins the first trick, he will get only three heart tricks, just as we have seen.

East should play the ten of hearts at the first trick, allowing South to win with the jack.

West gets in early with a diamond and leads his other heart, whereupon East takes four heart tricks to defeat the contract. (If South decides not to develop the diamonds, he can take only eight tricks before giving up.)

73

Computer Loses to Player

"You and your probability!" was the greeting I got the other day from my garage mechanic. Whenever I drop in, Joe (he seems to have been born without a second name) describes the events of his latest bridge game in such detail as would make a barber beg for mercy.

South dealer   **Both sides vulnerable**

NORTH
- ♠ J 9 4
- ♡ J 8
- ◇ A J 8 4
- ♣ K Q J 5

WEST
- ♠ 8 5
- ♡ 2
- ◇ Q 10 9 5 2
- ♣ 7 6 4 3 2

EAST
- ♠ Q 6 3
- ♡ A 7 6 4 3
- ◇ 7 3
- ♣ A 10 9

SOUTH-D
- ♠ A K 10 7 2
- ♡ K Q 10 9 5
- ◇ K 6
- ♣ 8

Defense Tricks:

□ □ □ □ □ □ □ □ □ □ □ □ □

Bid the hand your way:

North	East	South	West
_____	_____	_____	_____
_____	_____	_____	_____
_____	_____	_____	_____
_____	_____	_____	_____
		Opening Lead _____	

74

How the hand was bid:

SOUTH	WEST	NORTH	EAST
1 ♠	Pass	2 ♣	Pass
2 ♡	Pass	2 NT	Pass
4 ♡	Pass	4 ♠	All Pass

Opening lead — ♡ 2

How the hand was played: Joe showed me only the South hand and the dummy. "West leads the deuce of hearts to the ace, and back comes the three of hearts. West ruffs with the five of spades. How d'ya like that?"

"West leads the three of clubs, and East wins with the ace. Back comes the ten of clubs, and West plays the deuce. Play the hand."

"It's easy," I observed. "I win the trick in dummy with the queen of clubs." And I started to walk away.

"I once saw a wise guy driving around, and the bottom dropped out of his car," Joe remarked coldly. So I walked back and took a second look at the hand.

TRUMP PLAY

"It's a question of how to play the trumps," Joe pointed out. "After West has ruffed once do you bang down the ace and king of trumps or do you take a finesse for the queen?"

No matter what mathematics may tell you, East has the queen of spades. If he had only small spades, he would lead another heart instead of that futile ten of clubs.

If East has the queen of spades, he doesn't want to lead back another heart and make it obvious that his partner cannot over-ruff the dummy. That's the only sensible explanation of that silly club return.

Once you work it out that East has the queen of spades you must take a finesse to avoid the loss of a trump trick. It's fine points like this that keep your car in good condition.

Bad Trump Break May Be Stood Off

Gazing into another person's eyes is considered a good move in one of the world's favorite indoor sports. It's good at bridge too, but not as good as thinking.

South dealer   **Both sides vulnerable**

```
                    NORTH
                 ♠ A 8 7 6 4
                 ♡ Q 10 6
                 ◇ 8 2
                 ♣ A Q 10

    WEST                        EAST
 ♠ Q 3 2                     ♠ None
 ♡ 8 7 4                     ♡ 5 3 2
 ◇ Q J 10 5                  ◇ 9 7 6 4 3
 ♣ 6 5 3                     ♣ K 8 7 4 2

                    SOUTH-D
                 ♠ K J 10 9 5
                 ♡ A K J 9
                 ◇ A K
                 ♣ J 9
```

Defense Tricks:

☐ ☐ ☐ ☐ ☐ ☐ ☐ ☐ ☐ ☐ ☐ ☐ ☐

Bid the hand your way:

North	East	South	West
_____	_____	_____	_____
_____	_____	_____	_____
_____	_____	_____	_____
		_____	

                                  Opening Lead _____

How the hand was bid:

SOUTH	WEST	NORTH	EAST
1 ♣	Pass	3 ♣	Pass
4 ◇	Pass	4 ♠	Pass
5 ♡	Pass	6 ♠	All Pass
			Opening lead — ◇ Q

How the hand was played: South won the first trick with the king of diamonds and led the jack of spades from his hand. West calmly played a low spade.

South stared West right in the eye, and West stared right back. It might have been a touching sight, except that both were men and neither was exactly a beauty.

Eventually South played the ace of spades from dummy. East discarded a diamond, and South moaned like a garroted gnu. South lost a spade and a club, for a score of minus 100 instead of plus 1430. So much for the value of staring an opponent in the eye.

SPADE PLAY

The slam depended on the correct spade play. At the second trick, South should lead the king of spades.

If it turns out that West has all the missing trumps (as in this hand), South discovers the bad break and can next lead the jack of spades through West's queen.

What if East has all three trumps? South takes the king and ace of trumps, cashes the ace of diamonds and runs his hearts. If East fails to ruff, South leads a third round of trumps to put East in the lead. Now East must give dummy a free club finesse or must lead a red card to let dummy ruff while South discards a club.

The point is that South can rely on this end play if East has all of the trumps. He has no such end play if West has the trumps, so he must play the spades in such a way as to preserve a finesse against West.

77

Thoughtful Player Needs Good Nose

A good nose will help you at the bridge table. If your opponent makes a peculiar play and you detect a strong aroma of herring, stop and think. The nose may not tell you what to think, but at least it will tell you when to think.

South dealer   **North-South vulnerable**

NORTH
♠ Q 6 3
♡ A Q 5
◇ J 7
♣ Q 9 8 5 2

WEST   EAST
♠ 10 9 8 4   ♠ A 2
♡ 9 7 6 3   ♡ 8
◇ A 8 4   ◇ 10 9 6 3 2
♣ K 7   ♣ A 10 6 4 3

SOUTH-D
♠ K J 7 5
♡ K J 10 4 2
◇ K Q 5
♣ J

Defense Tricks:

☐ ☐ ☐ ☐ ☐ ☐ ☐ ☐ ☐ ☐ ☐ ☐ ☐

Bid the hand your way:

North	East	South	West
_____	_____	_____	_____
_____	_____	_____	_____
_____	_____	_____	_____
_____	_____	_____	_____

Opening Lead _____

How the hand was bid:

SOUTH	WEST	NORTH	EAST
1 ♡	Pass	2 ♣	Pass
2 ♡	Pass	3 ♡	Pass
3 NT	All Pass		

Opening lead — ♠ 10

How the hand was played: West opened the ten of spades, and East won with the ace. East returned the deuce of spades, and South won with the king.

Now South led the five of diamonds, and West's nose began to twitch. This unexpected play had a very fishy smell.

West thought about the spades. The return of the deuce of spades showed an original holding of either two or four spades. But if East had started with A-J-x-x of spades, he would not have played the ace at the first trick; he would have kept the ace to capture dummy's queen. Clearly, East had started with only A-2 of spades. South therefore had started with K-J-x-x and was sure to win three spades.

COUNTS TRICKS

West thought next about the hearts. South had rebid his suit, showing at least a five-card suit. It was dollars to doughnuts that South was ready to run five heart tricks as soon as he wanted to.

West counted declarer's tricks: five hearts and three spades. Why was he making this peculiar diamond play?

South clearly was trying to steal his ninth trick. If he got a diamond trick, he would then run the spades and hearts. Hence South surely had K-Q-x of diamonds.

This left room for only one club in the South hand. So West stepped up with the ace of diamonds, laid down the king of clubs and led another club to defeat the contract.

Never underestimate the power of a nose.

Yield Trick Gracefully

"Not through the Iron Duke," East remarked as he played the king of spades at the first trick. East prided himself on having a remark for every occasion; it was too bad he didn't have an equal number of good plays.

South dealer   **Both sides vulnerable**

                              NORTH
                              ♠ Q J 4
                              ♡ J 3 2
                              ◇ J 6
                              ♣ K 9 6 5 3

        WEST   EAST
        ♠ 9 8 7 6   ♠ K 10 5
        ♡ 5   ♡ Q 10 9
        ◇ A Q 10 8 7   ◇ 9 5 3 2
        ♣ 8 7 2   ♣ Q J 10

                              SOUTH-D
                              ♠ A 3 2
                              ♡ A K 8 7 6 4
                              ◇ K 4
                              ♣ A 4

Defense Tricks:

☐ ☐ ☐ ☐ ☐ ☐ ☐ ☐ ☐ ☐ ☐ ☐ ☐ ☐

Bid the hand your way:

North	East	South	West
_____	_____	_____	_____
_____	_____	_____	_____
_____	_____	_____	_____
_____	_____	_____	_____
		Opening Lead _____	

How the hand was bid:

SOUTH	WEST	NORTH	EAST
1 ♡	Pass	2 ♡	Pass
4 ♡	All Pass		

Opening lead — ♠ 9

How the hand was played: South gratefully won the first trick with the ace of spades. He was, of course, sure to win two spade tricks no matter how the play went, but he was delighted to have a spade entry to the dummy.

Declarer drew two rounds of trumps with the ace and king, noting with disappointment that he had to lose a trump trick eventually. Then he cashed the top clubs and ruffed a club.

As it happened, the club broke 3-3, so that dummy's last two clubs were good. Since declarer could get back to dummy with the jack of spades, he could not lose his contract.

GIVES UP TRUMP

South actually led a trump, giving East his trick. If East were foolish enough to return a spade, South would make an over-trick. East actually led a diamond, giving West his two tricks, but declarer then got to dummy with the jack of spades to discard his losing spade on a good club.

Go back to the first trick and see what happens if East plays his low spade instead of covering dummy's queen with the king. South gets his spade trick in dummy too early.

Declarer leads out the top trumps but then cannot get back to the dummy's clubs even if he succeeds in setting them up. He must lose a trump, a spade and two diamonds.

Look for this sort of position in actual play. If you must give the opponents a trick, hand it over before it can be used effectively.

Gain Valuable Time with Key Play

No matter how clean a life you lead, the opponents will sometimes make the killing opening lead. Even then, however, you
may be able to maneuver so as to gain the time you need.

South dealer   **Neither side vulnerable**

NORTH
♠ K Q J 10
♡ 10 8 3 2
◊ J 10 4
♣ K 9

WEST
♠ A 9 8 6 4
♡ Q 6 4
◊ 8 7 6
♣ 10 7

EAST
♠ 7 5 3
♡ 7
◊ K Q 9 2
♣ Q J 5 4 3

SOUTH-D
♠ 2
♡ A K J 9 5
◊ A 5 3
♣ A 8 6 2

Defense Tricks:

☐ ☐ ☐ ☐ ☐ ☐ ☐ ☐ ☐ ☐ ☐ ☐ ☐ ☐

Bid the hand your way:

North	East	South	West
_____	_____	_____	_____
_____	_____	_____	_____
_____	_____	_____	_____
_____	_____	_____	_____
		Opening Lead _____	

How the hand was bid:

SOUTH	WEST	NORTH	EAST
1 ♡	Pass	1 ♠	Pass
2 ♣	Pass	3 ♡	Pass
4 ♡	All Pass		

Opening lead — ◊ 8

How the hand was played: If West had led anything but a diamond, life would have been very simple for South. He would have drawn two rounds of trumps and led spades to obtain discards for his two losing diamonds.

As it happened, West was unkind enough to lead the eight of diamonds. Declarer played the ten from dummy, and East covered with the queen.

South now fell from grace by winning with the ace of diamonds. This greedy play cost him his contract.

Declarer continued with the ace and king of trumps, but the queen failed to fall. He then led a spade, and West stepped up with the ace.

TAKE TWO DIAMONDS

West cashed the queen of hearts, and East discarded a low club to discourage a shift to that suit. West thereupon led another diamond and East took two diamond tricks, defeating the contract.

South makes the contract if he lets East hold the first trick with the queen of diamonds. East cannot return a diamond since then dummy's jack would win a trick. East's only chance is to return a trump.

Declarer takes two top trumps and leads a spade. West can take the ace of spades, but South still has the ace of diamonds. The defenders can get a trump, a spade and only their first diamond trick. South can get to dummy with the king of clubs to discard his losers on the good spades.

Expert Knows Right Hand from Left

People are so nosy nowadays that you can't stop the right hand from knowing what the left hand is doing. The modern proverb should read: Let not the right hand mess about in what the left hand doeth. As usual, there's a bridge hand to reinforce this elegant advice.

West dealer   **Neither side vulnerable**

NORTH
- ♠ 7 4 3
- ♡ Q J 6 3
- ◇ 8 7 3
- ♣ 9 8 4

WEST-D   EAST
- ♠ 6 2   ♠ Q 10
- ♡ A 9 2   ♡ 8 7 5 4
- ◇ A Q J 9   ◇ 6 5 4 2
- ♣ Q J 10 2   ♣ K 7 3

· SOUTH
- ♠ A K J 9 8 5
- ♡ K 10
- ◇ K 10
- ♣ A 6 5

Defense Tricks:

☐ ☐ ☐ ☐ ☐ ☐ ☐ ☐ ☐ ☐ ☐ ☐ ☐ ☐

Bid the hand your way:

North	East	South	West
_____	_____	_____	_____
_____	_____	_____	_____
_____	_____	_____	_____
_____	_____	_____	_____
		Opening Lead _____	

84

How the hand was bid:

WEST	NORTH	EAST	SOUTH
1 ◇	Pass	2 ◇	Double
3 ◇	Pass	Pass	3 ♠
All Pass			

Opening lead — ♣ Q

How the hand was played: West opens the queen of clubs, and you see you are in danger of losing two clubs and the two red aces at the very least. People have been known to lose a trump trick in circumstances like yours, and there is even some danger of losing two diamonds instead of only one.

Since all readers of this book have the courage of lions (and also since you have surely noticed that the trumps are going to make no fuss), you do not flinch. You win the first trick with the ace of clubs and look around for something clever to do.

Your next move had better be really brilliant, for if you win the first trick with the ace of clubs you have already given the right-hand opponent his chance to mess about.

WILL LEAD DIAMONDS

Sooner or later you must draw trumps and knock out the ace of hearts. If West can get the lead to his partner, by way of the king of clubs, East will return a diamond. And there goes your contract, my lionhearted friend.

Now go back to the first trick and try being a rabbit instead of a lion. Refuse that first trick. If West continues with the jack of clubs, refuse that also. Save the ace of clubs to capture East's king.

You are quite willing to let West win the two club tricks that the defenders are sure to take. Whenever you do get in, you will draw trumps and lead the king of hearts. Since East cannot lead through your king of diamonds, the defenders can get only two clubs and two red aces.

Rescue Partner by Prompt Action

The advantage of studying foreign languages is that you know how to say "Goodbye" in the proper language if the person standing next to you happens to fall overboard. It might be even better to study something else (perhaps a bridge column) to prevent the accident altogether.

South dealer   Neither side vulnerable

NORTH
- ♠ Q 6 4 3
- ♡ 6 5 2
- ◊ 8 6 4
- ♣ K Q 6

WEST
- ♠ 8
- ♡ A Q J 7
- ◊ Q J 9 7
- ♣ J 9 5 2

EAST
- ♠ 7 5 2
- ♡ 8 4 3
- ◊ K 10 5 3
- ♣ 7 4 3

SOUTH-D
- ♠ A K J 10 9
- ♡ K 10 9
- ◊ A 2
- ♣ A 10 8

Defense Tricks:

☐ ☐ ☐ ☐ ☐ ☐ ☐ ☐ ☐ ☐ ☐ ☐ ☐

Bid the hand your way:

North	East	South	West
_____	_____	_____	_____
_____	_____	_____	_____
_____	_____	_____	_____
_____			_____

Opening Lead _____

86

How the hand was bid:

SOUTH	WEST	NORTH	EAST
1 ♠	Pass	2 ♠	Pass
4 ♠	All Pass		

Opening lead — ◇ Q

How the hand was played: West opened with the queen of diamonds, and East signalled encouragement with the five. This was a polite gesture, but West was overboard.

South refused the first diamond, won the second and drew three rounds of trumps. He ruffed dummy's last diamond and ran the three clubs, ending in dummy.

With the stage thus set, declarer led a heart from dummy. East played low, of course, and South played the nine.

BEYOND RESCUING

West now was beyond rescuing. If West led hearts, South would win a trick with the king. If West led anything else, dummy would ruff while South got rid of a heart. Either way South would lose only two hearts and one diamond.

We must admit that East was polite at the first trick. If East were vigorous and effective, he would play the king of diamonds on his partner's queen. This play would prevent West from falling overboard.

If South refuses the first trick, East holds the lead and promptly returns a heart up to dummy's weakness. West takes one heart trick with the jack and exits safely with a club or diamond. South must eventually give up two more heart tricks.

Even if South wins the first diamond trick, he must lose a diamond later. East makes sure to win this with the ten in order to lead a heart. This prompt action rescues West from the end play.

Declarer Works Hard on Wrong Play

One of the pleasantest occupations in the world is to sit back and watch somebody else work. It's especially pleasant when you know the work isn't going to do a particle of good.

South dealer   **North-South vulnerable**

NORTH
♠ A 8 6 4
♡ A 10 5
◇ 7 6
♣ A 7 5 4

WEST   **EAST**
♠ 5 2   ♠ 10
♡ K Q J 9 2   ♡ 8 6 4
◇ A Q 5   ◇ J 10 9 8 4 3
♣ 9 6 3   ♣ Q J 10

SOUTH-D
♠ K Q J 9 7 3
♡ 7 3
◇ K 2
♣ K 8 2

Defense Tricks:

☐ ☐ ☐ ☐ ☐ ☐ ☐ ☐ ☐ ☐ ☐ ☐

Bid the hand your way:

North	East	South	West
_____	_____	_____	_____
_____	_____	_____	_____
_____	_____	_____	_____

Opening Lead _____

How the hand was bid:

SOUTH	WEST	NORTH	EAST
1 ♠	2 ♡	3 ♠	Pass
4 ♠	All Pass		

Opening lead — ♡ K

How the hand was played: South refused the first heart trick, and West continued with the jack of hearts. Declarer took dummy's ace and immediately led a low club from dummy.

East played the queen of clubs, and South hastened to win with the king. He drew two rounds of trumps and led a club towards dummy. West played low, and South put up dummy's ace with a shade of disappointment on his face.

Declarer shrugged his shoulders and led another club from dummy. He hoped that both opponents would follow suit, for then dummy's last club would be good. South also hoped that West would have to win the trick, for then nothing awkward would happend in diamonds.

WRONG PLAYER WINS

South's work did him no good, for the wrong player won. East took the third round of clubs and naturally led the jack of diamonds. Down one.

After winning the second heart, South must draw trumps with the king and queen, cashes the king and ace of clubs and then leads the ten of hearts from dummy. Instead of ruffing, South discards his losing club.

West wins the trick, but cannot defeat the contract. If West leads diamonds, South will get a trick with the king. If West leads hearts, dummy ruffs while South discards a diamond.

West's only safe play is a club. Even then, South can ruff. If West is short in clubs, he must lead a heart or diamond; South is beaten only if West started with four or more clubs.

Don't Play against Mind Readers

If the United States is seeking volunteers for a trip to Mars, they needn't count on me. I've already been there, and I didn't enjoy it. How can you play bridge with a mind reader?

South dealer   **Both sides vulnerable**

NORTH
♠ K 7
♡ A 10 5
♢ Q 8 5 3
♣ J 9 4 2

WEST   EAST
♠ Q J 10 5 2   ♠ 9 6 4 3
♡ J 7 6   ♡ Q 9 4 3
♢ 9 7   ♢ A 4
♣ 10 8 6   ♣ A 5 3

SOUTH-D
♠ A 8
♡ K 8 2
♢ K J 10 6 2
♣ K Q 7

Defense Tricks:

☐ ☐ ☐ ☐ ☐ ☐ ☐ ☐ ☐ ☐ ☐ ☐ ☐

Bid the hand your way:

North	East	South	West
_____	_____	_____	_____
_____	_____	_____	_____
_____	_____	_____	_____
_____	_____	_____	_____
		Opening Lead	_____

How the hand was bid:

SOUTH	WEST	NORTH	EAST
1 NT	Pass	3 NT	All Pass

Opening lead — ♠ Q

How the hand was played: Back on Earth I'd expect to make this contract about nine times out of ten. On Mars, where everybody is a telepath, I was licked before I started. "You didn't have an Earthman's chance," they told me later.

West opened the queen of spades. That's another trouble with bridge on Mars. They always make the best lead.

I could expect to win two spades, two hearts and four diamonds fairly easily. The trouble is that one spade stopper had to go at the first trick. If I then knocked out the ace of diamonds, they'd return a spade.

This would limit me to eight tricks. Whenever I tried to develop a club trick, the enemy could take the spades.

OUT ON A STEAL

I tried my familiar Earthy tactics. I won the first trick in dummy with the king of spades and led the jack of clubs.

On Earth, East would play low in the hope that I was going to try a losing finesse of some kind. That would give me one club trick; and I would switch to diamonds and get nine tricks before the spades could be brought in.

But it didn't work on Mars. My right-hand opponent snickered; and let me tell you—a Martian snicker is not a pleasant sound for a teetotaller to hear. "That went out with sex," he chortled. (They're very advanced on Mars.)

And he took the ace of clubs and returned a spade. That was the end of me and of the bridge game.

From here on I'm going to keep my feet on the Earth, where I can steal a trick when I need it.

Play Hand like Western Ranger

The generation now growing up may view everything in terms of the old Western movies. All people will be considered either desperadoes, maidens or Rangers. And the bridge hand of the future will look like the following diagram.

South dealer   **Both sides vulnerable**

NORTH
♠ A J 9 6
♡ K 9 3
◇ 10 9 4
♣ 9 5 3

WEST   EAST
♠ K 10 7 2   ♠ Q 5 4
♡ 5   ♡ 8 7 6 2
◇ K 6   ◇ 7 5 2
♣ K Q J 10 4 2   ♣ A 8 7

SOUTH-D
♠ 8 3
♡ A Q J 10 4
◇ A Q J 8 3
♣ 6

Defense Tricks:

☐ ☐ ☐ ☐ ☐ ☐ ☐ ☐ ☐ ☐ ☐ ☐ ☐

Bid the hand your way:

North	East	South	West
_____	_____	_____	_____
_____	_____	_____	_____
_____	_____	_____	_____
_____	_____	_____	_____
		Opening Lead	_____

How the hand was bid:

SOUTH	WEST	NORTH	EAST
1 ♡	2 ♣	2 ♡	Pass
4 ♡	All Pass		

Opening lead — ♣ K

How the hand was played: West opens the king of clubs and continues with another club. South ruffs, cashes the ace of trumps and leads a trump to dummy's king.

The desperado draws two more rounds of trumps, reducing the hand to notrump. Now comes a spade to dummy's ace and a diamond finesse, losing to the king. The defenders take their black cards, and South is down three!

MAIDEN MUDDLES

The maiden muddles the hand, just as you might expect from watching a Western movie. When the bad trump break shows up, she abandons trumps in order to try the diamond finesse early. This is a good move.

A bad move is soon to follow. West wins the first diamond and leads another club, whereupon our maiden ruffs. Now she has one trump in each hand and East has two trumps. Declarer leads diamonds until East ruffs. Now the defenders make a trick in each suit, and South is down one.

The Ranger plays the hand properly, as you might expect from the sort of fellow that wastes his time rescuing maidens from desperadoes. After two rounds of trumps, he tries the diamond finesse. When West leads back a club, the Ranger discards a spade instead of ruffing.

Now West may curl his mustache and snarl fiercely, but he can do no harm. If he leads another club, dummy ruffs; and South can easily draw trumps from his own hand. If West leads anything else, declarer wins, draws trumps and claims the rest.

Hiyo Silver!

Winning Play May Look Sour

I used to play tennis with people who would rather hit the ball "properly" than win the point. The same kind of person, when he plays bridge, tries to make the "proper" play even if it's sure to lose.

West dealer   **Both sides vulnerable**

NORTH
♠ A Q
♡ 5 3 2
◊ K J 10 6
♣ A 7 4 3

WEST-D   EAST
♠ J 10 9 8 7 4   ♠ K 5 3
♡ A 4   ♡ J 10 8
◊ A Q   ◊ 8 7 5 4 2
♣ J 10 5   ♣ 9 8

SOUTH
♠ 6 2
♡ K Q 9 7 6
◊ 9 3
♣ K Q 6 2

Defense Tricks:

☐ ☐ ☐ ☐ ☐ ☐ ☐ ☐ ☐ ☐ ☐ ☐

Bid the hand your way:

North	East	South	West
_____	_____	_____	_____
_____	_____	_____	_____
_____	_____	_____	_____
_____	_____	_____	_____
		Opening Lead	_____

94

How the hand was bid:

WEST	NORTH	EAST	SOUTH
1 ♠	Pass	Pass	2 ♡
Pass	4 ♡	All Pass	

Opening lead — ♠ J

How the hand was played: West opened the jack of spades, and the finesse lost to East's king. Back came a spade to the ace.

Declarer led a trump from dummy, East played low and South put up the queen. This was the "proper" play, but it was sure to lose. West took his two red aces, and East eventually won a trump trick with the jack to defeat the contract.

South's play was sure to lose because West surely had the ace of hearts.

WINNING PLAY

The winning play is to finesse with the nine of hearts on the first round of trumps. Normally, this is a ridiculous play; but in this hand it is South's only chance.

South is sure to lose two trump tricks if West has the ten or jack of hearts as well as the ace. South can hold the trump loss to one trick if East has both the ten and jack of hearts, and the way to do so is to finesse with the nine of hearts.

As it happens, this deep finesse drives out the ace of trumps. The trumps then break favorably, and South has no further problem.

When there's no other hope, be ready to make an unusual play—even a silly play. You might just as well be hanged for a goat as a sheep.

Reverse Rule to Prevent Overruff

When you want to ruff two or more cards in dummy, your general procedure is to begin by ruffing low and end by ruffing with a high trump. The theory is that the early ruff is not likely to be overruffed, so that dummy's low trump is good enough for the job. Sometimes you must work on the opposite tack.

North dealer   **Both sides vulnerable**

NORTH-D
♠ K 8
♡ K 6 5 2
♢ K 7
♣ A 10 9 6 5

WEST
♠ None
♡ Q J 10
♢ 10 8 6 5 2
♣ Q 8 7 4 2

EAST
♠ J 5 4 3 2
♡ A 9 8 7
♢ Q J
♣ K J

SOUTH
♠ A Q 10 9 7 6
♡ 4 3
♢ A 9 4 3
♣ 3

Defense Tricks:

☐ ☐ ☐ ☐ ☐ ☐ ☐ ☐ ☐ ☐ ☐ ☐

Bid the hand your way:

North	East	South	West
_____	_____	_____	_____
_____	_____	_____	_____
_____	_____	_____	_____
_____	_____	_____	_____

Opening Lead _____

How the hand was bid:

NORTH	EAST	SOUTH	WEST
1 ♣	Pass	1 ♠	Pass
1 NT	Pass	4 ♠	All Pass

Opening Lead — ♡ Q

How the hand was played: West opens the queen of hearts and continues the suit. You ruff the third heart and see that the contract is cold if you can ruff two diamonds in dummy. You are willing to lose one trick to the jack of spades, provided that you can go through with your ruffing plan.

If you are hasty about it, you will immediately cash the top diamonds and ruff a low diamond with dummy's eight of trumps. That is the end of your game.

East overruffs with the jack of spades and returns a trump. That removes dummy's last trump, so that you must eventually lose a diamond trick to West.

SAFER METHOD

There is a safer way to play the hand. After ruffing the third heart, cash dummy's ace of clubs and the high diamonds. Then lead a diamond from your hand and ruff in dummy with the king of spades.

This cannot be overruffed, and you can later ruff your other diamond with the eight of spades. You don't care about being overruffed later since only the jack of spades can do so and you are willing to lose that trick.

In fact, after you have ruffed a diamond with dummy's king of spades, ruff a club in your hand with the ace of spades. This protects you against any unusual distribution of the clubs. You cannot be overruffed.

Now you are in position to lead your last diamond and ruff in dummy. Game and rubber are assured.

Test Your Skill as Sleuth

Most bridge players are born criminals, and you get no thanks or praise for being on the other side of the law. Still, test your skill as a bridge detective. See if you can spot the crime and the criminal in the following hand.

North dealer   **Both sides vulnerable**

NORTH-D
♠ 10 5
♡ 7 6
◇ A K 9 8
♣ A K 10 7 3

WEST
♠ 7 2
♡ 5 3
◇ J 10 6 5 2
♣ J 6 4

EAST
♠ A K Q 9 6 3
♡ 9 8
◇ Q
♣ Q 9 8 2

SOUTH
♠ J 8 4
♡ A K J 10 4 2
◇ 7 4 3
♣ 5

Defense Tricks:

☐ ☐ ☐ ☐ ☐ ☐ ☐ ☐ ☐ ☐ ☐ ☐

Bid the hand your way:

North	East	South	West
_____	_____	_____	_____
_____	_____	_____	_____
_____	_____	_____	_____
_____	_____	_____	_____
		Opening Lead _____	

98

How the hand was bid:

NORTH	EAST	SOUTH	WEST
1 ◇	1 ♠	2 ♡	Pass
3 ♣	Pass	3 ♡	Pass
4 ♡	All Pass		

Opening lead — ♠ 7

How the hand was played: East won the first trick with the queen of spades and returned a trump. South's jack lost to the queen, and back came another trump. South drew a third trump, cashed the top clubs and ruffed a club. He got back to dummy with a diamond to ruff another club and then returned to dummy with the other high diamond to cash the last club. This gave South ten tricks: five trumps, two diamonds and three clubs.

The clues are all there, where you can see them. See what you can do with them before you read on.

DOUBLE CRIME

There are two crimes and two criminals. Don't be satisfied with just one.

West should defeat the contract after winning the second trick with the queen of hearts. He should return a diamond to take an entry out of dummy before the clubs can be started.

Now the clubs cannot be set up. Declarer gets only two club tricks instead of three. He goes down one instead of making game and rubber.

South was a criminal also for putting himself in jeopardy. Instead of finessing in trumps at the second trick, South should step up with the ace or king. He should cash two high clubs, discarding a spade, and ruff a club. Then he takes a high trump and gives up a trump trick.

Now South can surely bring in a third club trick to make the contract.

Don't Use One Suit If You Have Two

When you have two suits to work with you don't always have to
choose one or the other. Work out the play in such a way as to
have both.

North dealer   **East-West vulnerable**

NORTH-D

♠ J 9 8
♡ J 8 2
◇ K Q 10 7 6
♣ 6 3

WEST   EAST

♠ Q 10 7 3 2   ♠ 6 5 4
♡ K 10 7 4   ♡ Q 6 5
◇ 3 2   ◇ A 5 4
♣ 7 4   ♣ K 10 9 8

SOUTH

♠ A K
♡ A 9 3
◇ J 9 8
♣ A Q J 5 2

Defense Tricks:

☐ ☐ ☐ ☐ ☐ ☐ ☐ ☐ ☐ ☐ ☐ ☐ ☐

Bid the hand your way:

North	East	South	West
————	————	————	————
————	————	————	————
————	————	————	————
————		————	————

Opening Lead ———

How the hand was bid:

NORTH	EAST	SOUTH	WEST
Pass	Pass	1 ♣	Pass
1 ◊	Pass	2 NT	Pass
3 NT	All Pass		

Opening lead — ♠ 3

How the hand was played: South has two spades and one heart and therefore needs six tricks in diamonds and clubs combined to make the game contract.

The trouble with going after the diamonds hammer and tongs is that South cannot be sure of getting to dummy after knocking out the ace of diamonds. For example, South might lead the jack of diamonds and then another diamond in the hope that an opponent would be obliged to win the first or second diamond. Actually, East would refuse both tricks, and the diamonds would not come in.

It would then be too late to go after the clubs. Declarer would be able to lead clubs from dummy only once. One club finesse would not be enough to bring in four club tricks even though the finesse succeeds.

ENTRIES TO DUMMY

The correct play is to lead the jack of diamonds to dummy's king at the second trick. East holds up, and you can return a club from dummy to win a finesse with the queen.

Now lead the nine of diamonds to dummy's queen. If an opponent has to win the trick, you can get four diamond tricks and two clubs.

Since East holds up his ace of diamonds again, you are once more in dummy to take another club finesse. The jack of clubs wins, and you can continue with the ace of clubs and a low club.

Now you make four club tricks and two diamonds, enough for game.

101

Einstein Theory Helps at Bridge

According to the late Professor Albert Einstein, time is the fourth dimension. It's not enough to know where you're going; you have to know when to get there. If you don't believe it, we have a bridge hand to prove that Einstein was right.

South dealer   **Both sides vulnerable**

NORTH
- ♠ A K J 10 5
- ♡ K Q 10 9
- ◇ None
- ♣ K J 8 5

WEST
- ♠ 7 3
- ♡ 8 7 6 5
- ◇ K J 8 7 4 3
- ♣ 6

EAST
- ♠ Q 9 8 6 2
- ♡ 3
- ◇ Q 9 5
- ♣ 10 9 4 2

SOUTH-D
- ♠ 4
- ♡ A J 4 2
- ◇ A 10 6 2
- ♣ A Q 7 3

Defense Tricks:

☐ ☐ ☐ ☐ ☐ ☐ ☐ ☐ ☐ ☐ ☐ ☐ ☐

Bid the hand your way:

North	East	South	West
_____	_____	_____	_____
_____	_____	_____	_____
_____	_____	_____	_____
_____	_____	_____	_____
		Opening Lead _____	

102

How the hand was bid:

SOUTH	WEST	NORTH	EAST
1 ♡	Pass	2 ♠	Pass
3 ♣	Pass	3 ♡	Pass
4 ◇	Pass	4 NT	Pass
5 ♠	Pass	7 ♡	All Pass
		Opening lead — ♡ 8	

How the hand was played: When this hand was played in a recent team match, the bidding and the first three tricks were the same at both tables. The nine of hearts won the first trick, the ace of spades took the second and then declarer ruffed a low spade with the ace of trumps.

The first declarer led his remaining low trump to dummy's ten immediately after ruffing the first spade. Then he ruffed another spade with the jack of hearts. West, out of spades, discarded his singleton club.

That was the end of the grand slam. South could not get back to dummy to draw trumps. If he led a club, West would ruff. If South ruffed a diamond in dummy, West would wind up with one trump more than either dummy or declarer.

LEADS CLUB FIRST

At the other table the declarer was Don Krauss, young Los Angeles expert (and a student of Einsteinian theory). After ruffing the first spade, Krauss got back to dummy immediately by leading a club to the king.

It was safe to do so at this time. It would not be safe later. The card was the same; only the time was different.

Krauss ruffed another spade with the jack of hearts and still had his low trump to lead to dummy. It was easy to draw trumps and take the rest of the tricks with high cards.

It just shows what you can do with a deck of cards if you study Einstein.

Make Allowance for Bad Breaks

The correct way to play a suit depends partly on the number of tricks you need. The point is illustrated by one of the hands played in the 1964 Bridge Olympics.

North dealer   **North-South vulnerable**

NORTH-D
♠ K 9 2
♡ 5
♢ K Q 2
♣ K J 9 6 5 2

WEST   EAST
♠ Q 10 8 4   ♠ 7 6 5 3
♡ A   ♡ J 10 9 7
♢ A 10 9 3   ♢ J 7 4
♣ Q 10 7 3   ♣ 8 4

SOUTH
♠ A J
♡ K Q 8 6 4 3 2
♢ 8 6 5
♣ A

Defense Tricks:

□ □ □ □ □ □ □ □ □ □ □ □ □

Bid the hand your way:

North	East	South	West
		Opening Lead	___

How the hand was bid:

NORTH	EAST	SOUTH	WEST
1 ♣	Pass	1 ♡	Pass
2 ♣	Pass	4 ♡	All Pass
			Opening lead — ♠ 4

How the hand was played: West opens the four of spades, and declarer wins with the jack. South cashes both black aces and then leads a diamond.

West must step up with the ace of diamonds and then returns a diamond to dummy's queen. At this stage, declarer's only problem is to limit the trump loss to two tricks.

Declarer leads the trump from dummy, and East plays the jack. South should play the queen if the contract is five hearts, but should play low at the actual contract.

LOSES THREE TRUMPS

If South plays the queen of hearts, he will lose to the ace. South will later draw the seven on his king of hearts but will then have to lose tricks to the ten and nine. South thus loses three trump tricks—and his contract.

If the five missing trumps are divided 3-2, South can afford to play low on the first trump trick. The ace will not fall in this case, but South can later lead the king of hearts to drive out the ace; then he can finish drawing the trumps by leading the queen of hearts.

If the trumps are 4-1, South's only chance is that the singleton is the ace. As the cards lie, West must play the ace anyway. South can later draw two rounds of trumps with the king and queen and can give up one other trump trick to East.

South would correctly play the queen of hearts on the first trump trick if he could afford to lose only one trump. Then he would have to play East for the doubleton ace of trumps.

Choose Finesses When Entries Are Short

Some day a clever politician will win an election by promising the bridge players all the finesses they can take. Until that time, we must get along with the finesses we have entries for.

West dealer   **North-South vulnerable**

NORTH
- ♠ A 7 6 2
- ♡ 6 5 3
- ♢ 7 4 2
- ♣ A 8 3

WEST-D
- ♠ K Q J 10 3
- ♡ 4
- ♢ 10 6 3
- ♣ Q J 9 4

EAST
- ♠ 9 4
- ♡ K 8 7 2
- ♢ K 9 8 5
- ♣ 10 6 2

SOUTH
- ♠ 8 5
- ♡ A Q J 10 9
- ♢ A Q J
- ♣ K 7 5

Defense Tricks:

☐ ☐ ☐ ☐ ☐ ☐ ☐ ☐ ☐ ☐ ☐ ☐ ☐

Bid the hand your way:

North	East	South	West
_____	_____	_____	_____
_____	_____	_____	_____
_____	_____	_____	_____
_____	_____	_____	_____

Opening Lead _____

How the hand was bid:

WEST	NORTH	EAST	SOUTH
Pass	Pass	Pass	1 ♡
1 ♠	Pass	Pass	Double
Pass	1 NT	Pass	2 ♡
Pass	3 ♡	Pass	4 ♡
All Pass			

Opening lead — ♠ K

How the hand was played: West opened the king of spades, and South saw he was going to reach dummy twice—once with each ace. He could take exactly two finesses.

South really wanted to finesse twice in hearts and twice more in diamonds. Since the government didn't guarantee him four finesses, he had to choose two.

Declarer decided to try the hearts. He won the first trick with dummy's ace of spades and led a heart to win a finesse with the queen. He got back to dummy with the ace of clubs and tried another heart finesse.

FINESSE WORKS

The finesse succeeded, but the contract failed. When West showed out of trumps, South realized that two trump finesses did him no good. He still had to lose a trump trick. South had to play the diamonds out of his hand and wound up losing a trick in each suit. Down one.

Declarer made the wrong decision when he chose to finesse in hearts. Even though he won both finesses, he still gained nothing. If he had taken two successful diamond finesses, he would have gained a trick. He could then give up one trump by playing the suit from his own hand.

Even if South happens to lose the diamond finesse, he can still get back to dummy with a club and take one heart finesse. This will make the contract if East has K-x of hearts. This is more likely than losing the heart finesse first and then finding K-x of diamonds in the East hand.

107

Dummy's Arrangement Fulfills Contract

Have you ever taken lessons in putting down your hand as the dummy? Don't throw the book down with the remark "Sheinwold's off his rocker." The contract may depend on whether you put high cards or low cards on top.

South dealer   **Both sides vulnerable**

```
                    NORTH
                    ♠ Q 10 9
                    ♡ K J 10 2
                    ◇ 6 5 4 3
                    ♣ A K

      WEST                          EAST
      ♠ 6 5 3 2                     ♠ 8 7 4
      ♡ 7 4                         ♡ A Q 9 8 5
      ◇ A Q 7                       ◇ 9 8
      ♣ 7 6 3 2                     ♣ Q 8 5

                    SOUTH-D
                    ♠ A K J
                    ♡ 6 3
                    ◇ K J 10 2
                    ♣ J 10 9 4
```

Defense Tricks:

☐ ☐ ☐ ☐ ☐ ☐ ☐ ☐ ☐ ☐ ☐ ☐ ☐

Bid the hand your way:

North	East	South	West
_____	_____	_____	_____
_____	_____	_____	_____
_____	_____	_____	_____

Opening Lead _____

SOUTH	WEST	NORTH	EAST
1 ◇	Pass	1 ♡	Pass
1 NT	Pass	3 NT	All Pass

Opening lead — ♡ 7

How the hand was played: Declarer lost a heart finesse to the queen and then a diamond finesse to the queen. The defenders continued with a heart to the ace and a diamond to the ace. West then led the seven of diamonds to the ten, and South needed the rest of the tricks for his contract.

Prospects were not so good. South could expect to win three spades, one heart, two diamonds and two clubs. This came to the eminently respectable total of eight tricks, but South had bid for nine.

Fortunately for South, his partner had put the dummy down with the high diamonds on top. As a result, South had played the six, five and four of diamonds from dummy on the first three diamond tricks, leaving only the three of diamonds in dummy. This paved the way for a swindle.

CASHES TRICKS

South ran his high spades and clubs and then cashed the king of hearts, discarding a club from his hand. Now declarer led the three of diamonds from dummy, and East was in trouble. If South was going to win the trick, East wanted to save the queen of clubs; but if dummy was going to win the trick, East wanted to save the nine of hearts.

East might have come up with the right answer if dummy's diamond had been the six, but how could he expect a measly little three to win the fourth round of the suit?

So East discarded the nine of hearts, and dummy took the last trick with the deuce of hearts.

Now will you take lessons on putting down the dummy?

Simple Play Is Difficult

"Nothing is so difficult as simplicity," said the club Philosopher. We all hooted at him, of course, because he is full of these profound observations and spends half his time proving that Life is like a cup of tea. But this time he had a bridge hand to prove his point.

North dealer   **Both sides vulnerable**

NORTH-D
- ♠ 8
- ♡ 7
- ◊ A K Q 10 9 2
- ♣ K 10 6 5 2

WEST	EAST
♠ A 5 3 2	♠ 6 4
♡ K Q J 10 2	♡ 8 4 3
◊ 6	◊ 8 7 5 4
♣ A 7 4	♣ J 9 8 3

SOUTH
- ♠ K Q J 10 9 7
- ♡ A 9 6 5
- ◊ J 3
- ♣ Q

Defense Tricks:

☐ ☐ ☐ ☐ ☐ ☐ ☐ ☐ ☐ ☐ ☐ ☐

Bid the hand your way:

North	East	South	West
———	———	———	———
———	———	———	———
———	———	———	———
———	———	———	———

Opening Lead ———

110

How the hand was bid:

NORTH	EAST	SOUTH	WEST
1 ◊	Pass	1 ♠	2 ♡
Pass	Pass	4 ♠	All Pass

Opening lead — ♡ K

How the hand was played: West opened the king of hearts, and South won with the ace. South ruffed a heart in dummy and looked around for new worlds to conquer.

He started the diamonds, probably hoping that the missing five diamonds would break 2½—2½. If so, perhaps he would be able to discard half a card on dummy's third diamond.

There was no such luck, of course, since West ruffed the second diamond. West then cashed two heart tricks and eventually got his two black aces. South was down two.

SHOULD MAKE CONTRACT

"There was a simple play to make the contract," our Philosopher pointed out. "It was so simple that the poor fellow never thought of it."

South must refuse the first trick even though he has the ace of hearts opposite dummy's singleton. After this simple play, South has an easy time.

If West leads trumps, South can knock out the ace of trumps, win the ace of hearts, draw the rest of the trumps and take safe discards on the diamonds.

West's best chance is to lead another heart at the second trick. South ruffs in dummy and leads a club to the queen. West takes the ace of clubs and forces out the ace of hearts. Now South leads a diamond to dummy, discards his last heart on the king of clubs and ruffs a club to play trumps.

Perhaps our bridge teachers should give a course in Philosophy to their advanced players.

Start Side Suit before Trumps

When there are holes in both your trump suit and your best side suit begin work on the side suit before you draw trumps. Your two long suits will then help each other.

South dealer   **Neither side vulnerable**

NORTH
♠ A 9 4
♡ K 4 2
♦ 8 7 4 3
♣ 10 7 3

WEST
♠ 10 7 5 2
♡ Q J 9 8
♦ K Q J 5
♣ Q

EAST
♠ Q J 8 3
♡ 5
♦ 10 9 6 2
♣ J 9 8 5

SOUTH-D
♠ K 6
♡ A 10 7 6 3
♦ A
♣ A K 6 4 2

Defense Tricks:

☐ ☐ ☐ ☐ ☐ ☐ ☐ ☐ ☐ ☐ ☐ ☐

Bid the hand your way:

North	East	South	West
_____	_____	_____	_____
_____	_____	_____	_____
_____	_____	_____	_____
_____	_____	_____	_____
		Opening Lead _____	

How the hand was bid:

SOUTH	WEST	NORTH	EAST
1 ♡	Pass	2 ♡	Pass
4 ♡	All Pass		

Opening lead — ◊ K

How the hand was played: South won the ace of diamonds and drew two rounds of trumps with the king and ace of hearts. Since both of the long suits broke badly, this hasty work on the trumps proved South's undoing.

Declarer continued with the ace and king of clubs. West ruffed the king of clubs, drew dummy's last trump and forced South to ruff a diamond. South still had to lose two club tricks so was sure to go down one, but he ran out of trumps and thus went down two.

It was not a distinguished performance, and South didn't take a bow as he scored 100 points for the opponents. "I once knew a man during the war," North remarked dryly, "who could go down three on a hand like that. But I wouldn't want to find fault with the way you played it."

GOOD PARTNER

This meant that North was a good partner. We all like a partner who doesn't find fault. North wouldn't have found anything to say at all if South had played the clubs before drawing trumps.

Suppose South leads out the ace and king of clubs at the second and third tricks. West ruffs the king of clubs and returns a diamond, forcing South to ruff. South gives up a club to the jack and ruffs the diamond return.

Only now can South afford to draw two rounds of trumps. He then leads a low club to ruff in dummy. South returns to his hand with the king of spades and leads the last club.

West gets two trump tricks and East gets a club, but South easily wins the rest to fulfill the game contract.

Lead to Strength to Use Up Entry

It's usually a good idea to attack the enemy where he is weakest, but there are also times when you must strike at his strength. Sometimes the best way to kill the dummy is to use up its entries before they become effective.

South dealer   **Both sides vulnerable**

```
                          NORTH
                          ♠ Q 9 7
                          ♡ 8 6 2
                          ◇ A J 7 5 2
                          ♣ K 8

        WEST                              EAST
        ♠ 5                               ♠ 6 4
        ♡ K 7 4 3                         ♡ J 10 9
        ◇ 8 4 3                           ◇ K Q 9 6
        ♣ 10 7 6 5 2                      ♣ A Q 9 4

                          SOUTH-D
                          ♠ A K J 10 8 3 2
                          ♡ A Q 5
                          ◇ 10
                          ♣ J 3
```

Defense Tricks:

☐ ☐ ☐ ☐ ☐ ☐ ☐ ☐ ☐ ☐ ☐ ☐

Bid the hand your way:

North	East	South	West
_____	_____	_____	_____
_____	_____	_____	_____
_____	_____	_____	_____
_____	_____	_____	_____
		Opening Lead _____	

How the hand was bid:

SOUTH	WEST	NORTH	EAST
1 ♠	Pass	2 ♢	Pass
3 ♠	Pass	4 ♠	All Pass

Opening lead — ♣ 5

How the hand was played: When this hand was played recently in a Swedish tournament, West opened the five of clubs, and East won with the queen. East continued with the ace of clubs, and West followed with the deuce.

This told East that his partner had led a five-card suit and that South had no more clubs. East saw no problem; he switched to the jack of hearts, leading up to dummy's weakness.

This normal lead gave South the time he needed to set up one of dummy's diamonds. He stepped right up with the ace of hearts, led a diamond to dummy's ace and ruffed a diamond.

South continued with a low trump to dummy's seven, ruffed a diamond with a high trump and led another low trump to dummy's nine. He ruffed still another diamond with the king of trumps and led a trump to dummy's queen.

CASHES DIAMOND

By this time, dummy's last diamond was good, so declarer cashed it to get rid of a heart. This assured the game.

There was no need for East to lead hearts at the third trick. If East could shut out dummy's diamonds, South would have to give up any heart losers he might have.

The way to shut out the diamonds is to return a trump. Now South can ruff out the diamonds, but he is one entry short. He cannot get back to dummy for the last good diamond.

Opportunities Noticed in Tournaments

One of the reasons you will enjoy playing duplicate bridge is that good plays don't get lost quite so often. In rubber bridge we tend to go on to the next hand without noticing what opportunities were missed. In a duplicate game somebody may see the opportunity.

South dealer   **North-South vulnerable**

NORTH
- ♠ A J
- ♡ Q J 9 8 5
- ◇ A K Q
- ♣ J 9 8

WEST
- ♠ K 10 7 4
- ♡ 7 2
- ◇ 9 6 2
- ♣ 7 5 3 2

EAST
- ♠ 8 6 5 3 2
- ♡ 4 3
- ◇ 8 7 4
- ♣ K Q 10

SOUTH-D
- ♠ Q 9
- ♡ A K 10 6
- ◇ J 10 5 3
- ♣ A 6 4

Defense Tricks:

☐ ☐ ☐ ☐ ☐ ☐ ☐ ☐ ☐ ☐ ☐ ☐

Bid the hand your way:

North	East	South	West
_____	_____	_____	_____
_____	_____	_____	_____
_____	_____	_____	_____
_____	_____	Opening Lead	_____

116

How the hand was bid:

SOUTH	WEST	NORTH	EAST
1 ♡	Pass	3 ◇	Pass
3 NT	Pass	4 NT	Pass
5 ♡	Pass	6 ♡	All Pass

Opening lead — ♣2

How the hand was played: It's easy to see what would happen to this hand at rubber bridge. East's ten of clubs would drive out the ace at the first trick.

South would draw trumps, cash the top diamonds and get to his hand with a trump to discard a club from dummy on the jack of diamonds. Then South would hold his breath and take the spade finesse.

The spade finesse works, as the cards lie, so South makes his slam. A new rubber would begin while East and West were still grumbling about South's luck.

If this hand were played in a strong club duplicate game, the same cards would be played at many tables. If one table saw the right defense, all the other defenders would hear about it and profit from the lesson.

INTELLIGENT PLAY

Go back to the first trick to see the proper defense. East should play the queen of clubs instead of the ten. Simple, and safe, but what a devastating play!

South captures the queen of clubs with the ace, of course, and then is ready to bet the crown jewels that West has the ten of clubs. He doesn't know who has the king of spades.

Naturally, South bases his play on what he knows. He draws two rounds of trumps, cashes dummy's top diamonds and gets to his hand with a trump to discard dummy's jack of spades on the jack of diamonds. Then he confidently leads a club to take the "proven" finesse of the nine of clubs. East then takes his two club tricks, defeating the slam.

Don't Rely on Goldfish to Play Hand Properly

Long and patient observation has taught me that there is a difference between goldfish and bridge players. (Not all bridge players, just some of them.) In the interest of science, I offer my evidence—in the form of a bridge hand.

North dealer   **Both sides vulneable**

NORTH-D
- ♠ 4 3
- ♡ J 4
- ◇ A Q J 4 2
- ♣ A Q 3 2

WEST
- ♠ Q J 10
- ♡ A K Q 10
- ◇ 8 7
- ♣ J 8 7 4

EAST
- ♠ 7 2
- ♡ 7 5 2
- ◇ 10 9 6 5
- ♣ K 10 6 5

SOUTH
- ♠ A K 9 8 6 5
- ♡ 9 8 6 3
- ◇ K 3
- ♣ 9

Defense Tricks:

☐ ☐ ☐ ☐ ☐ ☐ ☐ ☐ ☐ ☐ ☐ ☐

Bid the hand your way:

North	East	South	West
_____	_____	_____	_____
_____	_____	_____	_____
_____	_____	_____	_____
_____	_____	_____	_____

Opening Lead _____

How the hand was bid:

NORTH	EAST	SOUTH	WEST
1 ♦	Pass	1 ♠	Pass
2 ♣	Pass	3 ♠	Pass
4 ♠	All Pass		

Opening lead — ♡ K

How the hand was played: West opens the king of hearts, and everybody follows suit. West leads the queen of spades, and if a goldfish happens to be playing the South hand, he cannot resist gobbling up that queen of spades.

That trick is the end of South. For example, suppose South takes two rounds of trumps and starts on the diamonds. He discards a heart on the third diamond, but West ruffs and takes two more heart tricks.

JUST AS BAD

It's just as bad for South if he takes the king of spades and leads a heart right back. West takes the trick and leads another trump.

South is no better off if he takes the first spade and starts the diamonds at once. West ruffs the third diamond and leads a club.

In short, all continuations lead to one poor goldfish floating on top of the water.

A bridge player doesn't gobble up that queen of spades at the second trick. He sees that he must surely lose one trump trick no matter how the trumps are divided. He is safe if he loses that trick immediately.

Now it is West who cannot find happiness. If West leads another trump, South can draw trumps and run the diamonds safely. If West, instead, leads hearts, dummy can ruff the third heart. Life is much easier for the bridge player than for the poor fish.

Crime Laboratory Sifts Reports

When most of my readers are sleeping peacefully in their beds, the lights are still burning in my little crime laboratory. Reports from all parts of the world come in and go under the microscope. And every day the word goes out: "Another crime."

South dealer   **North-South vulnerable**

NORTH
♠ 9 3
♡ K 10 9 2
◇ A K J 4
♣ 6 4 2

WEST
♠ A
♡ 8 7 5 3
◇ 9 3 2
♣ 10 9 8 7 3

EAST
♠ 8 6 2
♡ A J 4
◇ Q 10 8 7 5
♣ A 5

SOUTH-D
♠ K Q J 10 7 5 4
♡ Q 6
◇ 6
♣ K Q J

Defense Tricks:

☐ ☐ ☐ ☐ ☐ ☐ ☐ ☐ ☐ ☐ ☐ ☐ ☐

Bid the hand your way:

North	East	South	West
_____	_____	_____	_____
_____	_____	_____	_____
_____	_____	_____	_____
_____	_____	_____	_____
		Opening Lead	_____

How the hand was bid:

SOUTH	WEST	NORTH	EAST
1 ♠	Pass	2 ◊	Pass
2 ♠	Pass	2 NT	Pass
4 ♠	All Pass		

Opening lead — ♣ 10

How the hand was played: Take this report, for example, from far-off Sofia. A Bulgarian merchant was found in his shop with nineteen knives sticking in him but no sign of robbery. The question is: Was there foul play?

Accompanying the report is the account of a bridge hand played by the merchant. He was declarer on the hand shown in the diagram.

East won the first trick with the ace of clubs and returned the five of clubs to declarer's king. South led a trump, and West took the ace. Back came a club, and East ruffed. East thereupon cashed the ace of hearts, and the next thing anybody knew the air was full of knives.

DIFFICULT CASE

It was a difficult case, because it was hard to know why any law-abiding citizen would be carrying nineteen knives on his person. But then it came to light that the deceased merchant sold knives in his shop, and so the case was cleared up.

Justified homicide was the obvious verdict.

After winning the second trick with the king of clubs, South clearly should take dummy's top diamonds to discard the queen of clubs. Only after taking this discard was it safe to lead trumps.

After all, a man who plays bridge in a knife shop shouldn't throw tricks. (Old Bulgarian proverb.)

Next case.

Hold-Up Play from Defensive Angle

The hold-up play is one of the best-known maneuvers in the game, but very few players think about it from the defensive point of view. You should think about holding up when you are a defender and about discouraging declarer from using the hold-up play against you.

South dealer   **Both sides vulnerable**

                          NORTH
                          ♠ 8 2
                          ♡ 10 5 3
                          ◊ A J 10 9 7 3
                          ♣ J 6

          WEST   EAST
          ♠ J 10 6 5 4   ♠ A Q 7
          ♡ Q 9 4 2   ♡ J 8 7
          ◊ 8 5   ◊ K 4 2
          ♣ 3 2   ♣ Q 10 9 8

                          SOUTH-D
                          ♠ K 9 3
                          ♡ A K 6
                          ◊ Q 6
                          ♣ A K 7 5 4

Defense Tricks:

☐ ☐ ☐ ☐ ☐ ☐ ☐ ☐ ☐ ☐ ☐ ☐ ☐

Bid the hand your way:

North	East	South	West
_____	_____	_____	_____
_____	_____	_____	_____
_____	_____	_____	_____
_____	_____		_____
		Opening Lead _____

How the hand was bid:

SOUTH	WEST	NORTH	EAST
1 ♣	Pass	1 ◇	Pass
2 NT	Pass	3 NT	All Pass

Opening lead — ♠ 5

How the hand was played: West led the five of spades, and East won with the ace. When East returned the queen of spades, South refused the trick. East continued with his last spade, and South took the king.

South went to work on the diamonds, leading the queen for a finesse. East took the king of diamonds and returned a heart.

That was the end of the defense, since declarer had the rest of the tricks with dummy's diamonds and his own high cards in hearts and clubs.

The players went happily on to the next rubber, bless their hearts, never suspecting that East had given South the contract by making two serious errors in the defense. Both had to do with the hold-up play.

DECEPTIVE PLAY

East should make a deceptive play at the first trick. He should play the queen of spades instead of winning with the ace.

The play of the queen of spades will discourage South from holding up the king of spades. East will get the lead with the king of diamonds and can resume the spades by taking the ace and leading his other spade to West.

Whether or not South takes the king of spades at once, East should hold up his king of diamonds. If South takes a second finesse, he gets only one diamond trick. And even if South suspects what is going on, he gets only two tricks in the suit instead of five.

Veteran Knows His Cats

After thirty years of playing bridge, I am now ready to tell it to the world: Some opponents are pussycats, and others are dirty dogs. You can save thirty years if you take my word for this profound truth—but make sure you know one from the other.

South dealer   **Both sides vulnerable**

NORTH
♠ A 7 2
♡ Q 9 8 3
◇ 9 6 5 2
♣ Q 7

WEST   EAST
♠ 8 4 3   ♠ Q J 10 9
♡ 6   ♡ 7 4
◇ A K J 10 8 4   ◇ 7
♣ K J 8   ♣ 10 9 6 5 3 2

SOUTH-D
♠ K 6 5
♡ A K J 10 5 2
◇ Q 3
♣ A 4

Defense Tricks:

☐ ☐ ☐ ☐ ☐ ☐ ☐ ☐ ☐ ☐ ☐ ☐ ☐ ☐

Bid the hand your way:

North	East	South	West
——	——	——	——
——	——	——	——
——	——	——	——
——	——	——	——
		Opening Lead	——

How the hand was bid:

SOUTH	WEST	NORTH	EAST
1 ♡	2 ◇	2 ♡	Pass
4 ♡	All Pass		

Opening lead — ◇ K

How the hand was played: When this hand was played not long ago, West led three rounds of diamonds to start with. South ruffed the third diamond, drew trumps with the ace and queen and ruffed another diamond.

South then cashed two high spades and led a third spade, hoping that the trick would be won by a pussycat. As it happened, East—that dirty dog—won the third spade. East returned a club, and South had to lose a club trick.

"I'd have made it if he had held the king of clubs," South explained to his long-suffering partner. This was true, of course, but the bidding made it dollars to doughnuts that West was the pussycat with the king of clubs.

CAN MAKE CONTRACT

South can make the contract if he knows which animal to catch. After ruffing the third round of diamonds, South must lead out his remaining five trumps, discarding a low spade from dummy on the last trump.

As his last five cards West must save one diamond, two clubs and therefore only two spades. Declarer thereupon cashes the king and ace of spades and gives up a diamond trick to West, discarding the losing spade from his hand.

West must win the trick and lead away from the king of clubs no matter how pitifully he may mew. Declarer wins the last two tricks, making the contract.

Make Ruff Harmless by Early Play

If you can't stop a defender from ruffing, arrange matters so that he ruffs a trick you were going to lose anyway. This may be more important than drawing trumps immediately.

West dealer   **Both sides vulnerable**

```
                    NORTH
                    ♠ K J 6 3
                    ♡ A K
                    ◇ K 9 5
                    ♣ K Q 9 4

     WEST-D                        EAST
     ♠ A Q                         ♠ 9 4
     ♡ 8 5                         ♡ Q J 10 7 4
     ◇ Q J 10 7 6 3                ◇ 8
     ♣ A 7 2                       ♣ J 10 8 5 3

                    SOUTH
                    ♠ 10 8 7 5 2
                    ♡ 9 6 3 2
                    ◇ A 4 2
                    ♣ 6
```

Defense Tricks:

☐ ☐ ☐ ☐ ☐ ☐ ☐ ☐ ☐ ☐ ☐ ☐ ☐

Bid the hand your way:

North	East	South	West
_____	_____	_____	_____
_____	_____	_____	_____
_____	_____	_____	_____
_____	_____	_____	_____

Opening Lead _____

How the hand was bid:

WEST	NORTH	EAST	SOUTH
1 ◊	Double	1 ♡	1 ♠
2 ◊	4 ♠	All Pass	

Opening lead — ◊ Q

How the hand was played: South saw the danger of a diamond ruff, but he thought that leading trumps quickly was the best safety measure. He therefore won the first trick in his hand with the ace of diamonds to lead a trump at once.

West stepped up with the ace of spades and led the jack of diamonds. Declarer had to play dummy's king, and East ruffed. (If declarer played low from dummy, East would discard and ruff the next diamond.)

Eventually, South led clubs, and West took the ace of clubs and another diamond trick. Down one.

NO HURRY

There was no hurry about drawing trumps. The important thing was to win the first diamond trick with dummy's king. If East managed to ruff the next diamond, he would ruff only declarer's loser instead of a top diamond.

Declarer should lead the king of clubs from dummy at the second trick. West can take his ace of clubs and lead a diamond, but South plays low when East ruffs.

East cannot get a second ruff, because West's only entry is the ace of spades. When West gets in with the ace of spades, East has to follow suit with his last trump.

This kind of problem may occur even when the opening lead is less obviously dangerous. If West's opening lead is the eight of hearts, for example, declarer must not try to get to his hand with the ace of diamonds. He must lead the king of clubs from dummy so that he can get to his hand by way of a club ruff.

Praise Partner to Cover Own Faults

Kindness and patience are the essential qualities in the care and training of partners. Be ready with a word of praise now and then. It may cover up your own misdeeds.

North dealer   **Both sides vulnerable**

NORTH-D
♠ A 6
♡ 7 4 3
◇ Q J 10 9 7 4
♣ A Q

WEST	EAST
♠ Q 8 7 4 3	♠ J 2
♡ Q	♡ K 10 9 6 5 2
◇ 5	◇ A K 3
♣ 9 8 6 5 3 2	♣ 10 4

SOUTH
♠ K 10 9 5
♡ A J 8
◇ 8 6 2
♣ K J 7

Defense Tricks:

☐ ☐ ☐ ☐ ☐ ☐ ☐ ☐ ☐ ☐ ☐ ☐ ☐

Bid the hand your way:

North	East	South	West
_____	_____	_____	_____
_____	_____	_____	_____
_____	_____	_____	_____
_____	_____	_____	_____

Opening Lead _____

How the hand was bid:

NORTH	EAST	SOUTH	WEST
1 ◇	1 ♡	2 NT	Pass
3 NT	All Pass		

Opening lead — ♡ Q

How the hand was played: When this hand was played, West led the queen of hearts.

"It didn't happen to help us this time," East later remarked, "but it shows that you're a good partner. Just keep leading my suit and you'll be on Easy Street."

West glowed with pride, as South scored up the rubber and an overtrick. All of which proves that flattery may not defeat the contract but at least it makes your partner a cheerful loser.

East could have been a cheerful winner if he had paid more attention to his own play. East spared the six of hearts at the first trick as an encouraging signal, but South refused the first trick and West had no other heart to lead.

USELESS SWITCH

West had to switch to a different suit, but nothing could help him. The shift to clubs was won in dummy, and declarer naturally began to work on the diamonds.

When East took the king of diamonds he led another heart, and South won a finesse with the jack. Declarer then knocked out the other top diamond and could claim the rest.

As every alert reader has surely noticed, East deserved no praise for his play at the first trick. Instead of signalling with the six of hearts, East must overtake with the king.

East continues with another heart to force out one of declarer's stoppers. East later takes the king of diamonds and knocks out the ace of hearts. East gets in with the ace of diamonds in time to run the hearts.

Partners Discuss Wrong Mistake

When your partner pulls a boner, your best move is to say a consoling "Hard luck, old boy" (or old girl, as the case may be) and go on cheerfully to the next boner. Otherwise you may find yourself arguing about the wrong thing.

South dealer   **Both sides vulnerable**

NORTH
♠ 7 4 3
♡ K 5 3 2
◇ None
♣ A K J 10 9 5

WEST   EAST
♠ K 6 5   ♠ 10 9 8 2
♡ 4   ♡ Q 8 7 6
◇ A K Q 10 9 4   ◇ 7 3 2
♣ 8 6 3   ♣ 7 2

SOUTH-D
♠ A Q J
♡ A J 10 9
◇ J 8 6 5
♣ Q 4

Defense Tricks:

☐ ☐ ☐ ☐ ☐ ☐ ☐ ☐ ☐ ☐ ☐ ☐ ☐

Bid the hand your way:

North	East	South	West
_____	_____	_____	_____
_____	_____	_____	_____
_____	_____	_____	_____
_____	_____	_____	_____

Opening Lead _____

How the hand was bid:

SOUTH	WEST	NORTH	EAST
1 ♡	2 ◇	3 ◇	Pass
3 NT	Pass	4 ♡	Pass
4 ♠	Pass	6 ♡	All Pass
			Opening lead — ◇ K

How the hand was played: South ruffed the opening lead in dummy, cashed the king of hearts and led the three of hearts from dummy. East played low, and declarer looked up at the ceiling for inspiration.

It was a bad ceiling apparently, for South went up with the ace of hearts and lost his slam. South eventually went down two, and North lit into him.

"Why didn't you play the jack?" North demanded. "Don't you know about finesses?"

"Finesses sometimes lose," South defended himself. "If I lose the finesse and a trump comes back I haven't enough tricks. My play works whenever the trumps break 3-2, regardless of who holds the queen."

DISCUSSION CONTINUES

The discussion continued, with much reference to mathematics, inferences from the bidding and other highfalutin subjects. It was all a waste of time because they were arguing about the wrong trick.

Declarer made his mistake at the second trick when he cashed the king of hearts. The correct play is to lead a low trump and try an immediate finesse with the jack.

If the finesse works, South can lead a trump to the king and clear up the trumps. If the finesse loses, there will still be two trumps in dummy and even a trump return cannot stop South from ruffing another diamond in dummy. Then declarer can discard two diamonds and two spades on dummy's clubs after drawing trumps.

Players Should Be Selfish

The trouble with most of us is we're too unselfish. We're always thinking of others, never of ourselves. What we need, at the bridge table especially, is more selfishness. I wouldn't tell you this if I couldn't prove it with a bridge hand.

East dealer   **North-South vulnerable**

NORTH
♠ Q J 5 2
♡ K Q 8
◇ 7
♣ 10 8 6 5 2

WEST   **EAST-D**
♠ 3   ♠ A 10 9 8 7 6
♡ 7 6   ♡ A 3
◇ Q 9 8 6 5 3   ◇ K 10 4 2
♣ 9 7 4 3   ♣ Q

SOUTH
♠ K 4
♡ J 10 9 5 4 2
◇ A J
♣ A K J

Defense Tricks:

☐ ☐ ☐ ☐ ☐ ☐ ☐ ☐ ☐ ☐ ☐ ☐ ☐ ☐

Bid the hand your way:

North	East	South	West
_____	_____	_____	_____
_____	_____	_____	_____
_____	_____	_____	_____

Opening Lead _____

How the hand was bid:

EAST	SOUTH	WEST	NORTH
1 ♠	2 ♡	Pass	3 ♡
Pass	4 ♡	All Pass	

Opening lead — ♠ 3

How the hand was played: East won the first trick with the ace of spades and returned a spade for his partner to ruff. It was a fine beginning—two tricks already in the bag, and none for South. Maybe this was the day that declarer was never going to make a trick.

As you can see, East was a dreamer. By the time he woke up, declarer had scored the game and rubber.

It didn't matter what West led back at the third trick. South could win a club or a diamond and lead a trump. East could win with the ace of trumps, but West was now out of trumps; and the defenders were out of tricks. South could easily draw another trump and claim the rest.

TOO FAST

East was too fast to consider his partner's welfare when he returned a spade at the second trick. This play would give West a ruff, but East should have been thinking of a ruff for himself.

At the second trick, East must return his singleton club. South wins and returns a trump.

Now it is time for East to remember his partner. East takes the first trump trick with the ace and returns a spade for West to ruff. West is then in position to return a club, and East ruffs. This gives the defenders four tricks instead of only three.

The point is that West's ruffing trick is also an entry—the only entry to the West hand. East can make good use of that entry only if he first clears the singleton club out of his hand.

Thank Air Conditioning for Correct Play

Few bridge players recognize what the play of the cards owes to air conditioning. We are ready to applaud the coup but not the cool.

South dealer   **Neither side vulnerable**

NORTH
♠ None
♡ Q 9 8 7 5 4
♢ K J 5 2
♣ 7 4 3

WEST
♠ K Q J 10 7 6 2
♡ 3
♢ 3
♣ Q 9 8 5

EAST
♠ A 9 4 3
♡ 2
♢ Q 10 9 8 6
♣ K J 10

SOUTH-D
♠ 8 5
♡ A K J 10 6
♢ A 7 4
♣ A 6 2

Defense Tricks:

☐ ☐ ☐ ☐ ☐ ☐ ☐ ☐ ☐ ☐ ☐ ☐ ☐ ☐

Bid the hand your way:

North	East	South	West
_____	_____	_____	_____
_____	_____	_____	_____
_____	_____	_____	_____
_____	_____	_____	_____
		Opening Lead _____	

How the hand was bid:

SOUTH	WEST	NORTH	EAST
1 ♡	4 ♠	5 ♡	All Pass

Opening lead — ◊ 3

How the hand was played: When this hand was played, many years ago, air conditioning in the home was almost unknown. If you played bridge during the summer, you kept the windows open and the fans going.

Since the cards often blew off the table, you developed the habit of playing a high card while it was still in sight. That's why South played the jack of diamonds from dummy at the first trick. Otherwise, he feared, it might blow off the table and never again be heard from.

East covered with the queen of diamonds, and South won with the ace. And now South had to lose two clubs and a diamond. Down one.

It's clear that South wanted to try a finesse with the jack of diamonds, but what was his hurry? It must have been a very breezy day.

TODAY'S PLAY

Today's declarer would play a low diamond from dummy at the first trick and win with the ace in his hand. He would ruff a spade, return with a trump, ruff his other spade, cash the ace of clubs and give up a club.

As the cards lie, the opponents are now helpless. If West wins the second defensive club trick, he can lead only spades or clubs; dummy ruffs while South discards the losing diamond. If East wins the second club he can lead a diamond, but this gives dummy a free finesse—thanks to the presence of the jack of diamonds in the dummy.

South cannot be positive that the opening lead is a singleton, but if the diamond finesse is going to work at the first trick it will still work later on.

Hold-Up Play May Cost Trick

Your object as declarer is not necessarily to make as many tricks as possible in each suit but to make your contract. They're not always the same.

East dealer   **Both sides vulnerable**

```
                    NORTH
                    ♠ 10 2
                    ♡ Q 10 9
                    ◇ A 6 5 3
                    ♣ Q J 9 7
    WEST                            EAST-D
    ♠ Q 9 7 5 3                     ♠ K 8 6
    ♡ 7 6 4 3                       ♡ A 2
    ◇ 7                             ◇ Q 10 9 8 4
    ♣ 5 4 2                         ♣ A 8 3
                    SOUTH
                    ♠ A J 4
                    ♡ K J 8 5
                    ◇ K J 2
                    ♣ K 10 6
```

Defense Tricks:

☐ ☐ ☐ ☐ ☐ ☐ ☐ ☐ ☐ ☐ ☐ ☐ ☐ ☐

Bid the hand your way:

North	East	South	West
_____	_____	_____	_____
_____	_____	_____	_____
_____	_____	_____	_____
_____	_____	_____	_____

Opening Lead _____

136

How the hand was bid:

EAST	SOUTH	WEST	NORTH
1 ◇	1 NT	Pass	3 NT
All Pass			

Opening lead — ♠ 5

How the hand was played: When this hand was played, West opened a low spade and East put up the king. South pounced on the trick with the ace of spades, thus making sure of two spade tricks.

South led a heart to dummy's nine, losing to the ace. Back came a spade, and West allowed dummy's ten to win the trick.

Declarer returned a diamond from dummy to win a finesse with the jack, whereupon he was sure of three diamonds, two spades and three hearts. South had to lead a club in the attempt to get a ninth trick, whereupon East took the ace of clubs and led a spade to let West defeat the contract with the long spades.

SACRIFICE TRICK

The opening lead should make it clear that West has led from a long suit. You cannot afford to let the defenders get three spade tricks, but you can afford to lose two spades and the two missing aces.

For this reason you let East win the first trick with the king of spades. This costs you a spade trick but assures the contract.

East returns a spade, and you hold up again, finessing with the jack. West wins with the queen of spades but his hand is now entryless and therefore dead.

No matter what West does next you can knock out the ace of hearts and the ace of clubs, making the game with one spade, three hearts, three clubs and at least two diamonds.

Force Opponent to Rescue You

Even if you take pride in being self-reliant, you must sometimes allow others to do things for you. For example, there's no satisfaction in sitting on your own lap—even if you can find a way to do it. The same principle applies to bridge, where you must sometimes find a way to get help from an enemy.

South dealer   **Neither side vulnerable**

NORTH
- ♠ 10 3 2
- ♡ Q 5
- ◇ K 8 7 4
- ♣ Q 5 3 2

WEST
- ♠ None
- ♡ J 10 9 8 3
- ◇ J 9 6 3 2
- ♣ K 8 7

EAST
- ♠ J 9 6
- ♡ 7 6 4 2
- ◇ A 10 5
- ♣ A 10 9

SOUTH-D
- ♠ A K Q 8 7 5 4
- ♡ A K
- ◇ Q
- ♣ J 6 4

Defense Tricks:

☐ ☐ ☐ ☐ ☐ ☐ ☐ ☐ ☐ ☐ ☐ ☐ ☐

Bid the hand your way:

North	East	South	West
_____	_____	_____	_____
_____	_____	_____	_____
_____	_____	_____	_____

Opening Lead _____

How the hand was bid:

SOUTH	WEST	NORTH	EAST
1 ♠	Pass	1 NT	Pass
4 ♠	All Pass		

Opening lead — ♡ J

How the hand was played: You win the first trick with the king of hearts and lead out the ace of trumps. West discards a small diamond, and the first cloud appears in the sky.

You can set up dummy's king of diamonds, but you can't get to dummy to discard on it. If you try to lead everything out of your own hand, you will lose a diamond and three clubs.

The sun would shine again if you could persuade an opponent to start the clubs. Then you could surely win a club trick either with dummy's queen or your own jack.

Neither East nor West will do you this favor with the cheerful smile that you like to see on a friend's face. They'll try to make you lead the clubs first, so that you give them four tricks.

NO CHOICE

The solution to the problem is to give them no choice. After winning that first trump trick, cash the ace of hearts and then lead the queen of diamonds.

Somebody has to take the ace of diamonds, and you don't care which opponent has it. If a club comes back, you will lose only two club tricks. If a diamond comes back, you can win in dummy with the king of diamonds, discarding a club from your hand. If a heart comes back, you can ruff in dummy, throwing a club on the trick.

If East happens to hold the ace of diamonds, he can return a trump, but this does no harm. You can then win a trick in dummy with the ten of spades, after which you will discard a club on the king of diamonds.

Don't Waste Tears When Play Is Bad

Since nobody hears more hard-luck stories than a bridge expert, those of us who are tenderhearted are in danger of sinking under the weight of sorrow. Fortunately, nature has given us enough strength to bear the misfortunes of other people.

South dealer   **Neither side vulnerable**

NORTH
- ♠ J 9 5
- ♡ 7 6 5
- ◊ A J 6 5 2
- ♣ Q 7

WEST
- ♠ 6 3
- ♡ 9 2
- ◊ 8 4 3
- ♣ K 9 8 6 3 2

EAST
- ♠ 8 7 4
- ♡ A K 10 4
- ◊ K Q 10 9
- ♣ 10 4

SOUTH-D
- ♠ A K Q 10 2
- ♡ Q J 8 3
- ◊ 7
- ♣ A J 5

Defense Tricks:

☐ ☐ ☐ ☐ ☐ ☐ ☐ ☐ ☐ ☐ ☐ ☐ ☐

Bid the hand your way:

North	East	South	West
_____	_____	_____	_____
_____	_____	_____	_____
_____	_____	_____	_____
_____	_____	_____	_____

Opening Lead _____

140

How the hand was bid:

SOUTH	WEST	NORTH	EAST
1 ♠	Pass	2 ♠	Pass
4 ♠	All Pass		

Opening lead — ♡ 9

How the hand was played: If you have a few tears that you don't really need, prepare to shed them for South in this hand. South's bad luck started when West led a heart and ruffed the third round of the suit.

West got out with a diamond to dummy's ace. South drew two rounds of trumps with the ace and dummy's jack and then led the queen of clubs from dummy for a finesse.

The club finesse lost, and South had another hard-luck story to tell his friends. In my office I have two file cabinets labeled "Why can't I win a finesse?" Today's hand came from one of those cabinets.

NO EXCUSES

If you can't spare any tears for such stories, don't make excuses. South didn't deserve even a sigh because his contract was unbeatable.

After drawing just one round of trumps, South should stop. There is no need to draw a second round. Instead, South should lead the queen of hearts.

If West has a trump, he will ruff. Dummy will overruff, and the contract will depend on the club finesse. Thus South has lost nothing by leading the queen of hearts.

Actually, West would be unable to ruff. South would discard a club from dummy on the queen of hearts. Declarer cashes the ace of clubs and ruffs his two clubs in dummy, thus assuring the contract without a club finesse.

Give Up Trick at Right Time

If you find an opponent generous enough to let you play a hand twice, take time out for thought. You look silly if you pile a second mistake on top of the first.

South dealer   **Both sides vulnerable**

NORTH
♠ 7 6 3
♡ 9 5 4 3
♢ 7 6 4
♣ K 5 3

WEST   **EAST**
♠ 8 2   ♠ 9 5 4
♡ Q 10 7 6 2   ♡ J 8
♢ 10 5   ♢ K J 9 8
♣ J 10 9 6   ♣ 8 7 4 2

SOUTH-D
♠ A K Q J 10
♡ A K
♢ A Q 3 2
♣ A Q

Defense Tricks:

☐ ☐ ☐ ☐ ☐ ☐ ☐ ☐ ☐ ☐ ☐ ☐ ☐

Bid the hand your way:

North	East	South	West
_____	_____	_____	_____
_____	_____	_____	_____
_____	_____	_____	_____
_____	_____	_____	_____
		Opening Lead _____	

142

How the hand was bid:

SOUTH	WEST	NORTH	EAST
2 ♠	Pass	2 NT	Pass
3 ◊	Pass	3 ♠	Pass
4 NT	Pass	5 ♣	Pass
5 NT	Pass	6 ◊	Pass
6 ♠	All Pass		

Opening lead — ♣ J

How the hand was played: South took the ace of clubs, drew one trump, overtook his club in dummy and returned a diamond to try a finesse with the queen. When this worked, South smiled triumphantly, but there is nothing sillier than an ill-timed smile.

South drew a second trump, cashed the ace of diamonds and gave up a diamond. East promptly returned a trump, taking the last trump out of dummy. South eventually lost a second diamond trick to East. Down one.

"I should have drawn only one trump," South remarked.

"You can play it again if you let me double," East offered.

South tried it again without drawing a second round of trumps. When East won the third round of diamonds he led his last diamond, and West ruffed with the eight of spades, shutting dummy out. Down one again.

EXACT PLAY

South can make the hand by exact play. He takes the ace of clubs, draws one trump and then leads a low diamond. The key is to give up the *first* diamond trick rather than the *third*.

East returns a club to dummy's king, and declarer wins a diamond finesse with the queen. Now South can draw a second round of trumps. He cashes the ace of diamonds and ruffs a diamond in dummy. Fortunately for him, the opponent with four diamonds also has the third trump.

143

Unlucky Players Shouldn't Guess

Some people are so unlucky they could not guess what day of
the week it is even if you gave them seven chances. Don't
despair if you belong in this unfortunate group. You'll do better
on some hands if you don't guess at all.

South dealer   **Both sides vulnerable**

NORTH
♠ J 7
♡ A J 8 4
◇ J 8 5
♣ A J 5 2

WEST   EAST
♠ 8 6 4   ♠ 10 9 5 3 2
♡ Q 5 3   ♡ 6 2
◇ A K 4 2   ◇ 9 7 6 3
♣ Q 7 4   ♣ 8 3

SOUTH-D
♠ A K Q
♡ K 10 9 7
◇ Q 10
♣ K 10 9 6

Defense Tricks:

☐ ☐ ☐ ☐ ☐ ☐ ☐ ☐ ☐ ☐ ☐ ☐ ☐

Bid the hand your way:

North	East	South	West
_____	_____	_____	_____
_____	_____	_____	_____
_____	_____	_____	_____

Opening Lead _____

How the hand was bid:

SOUTH	WEST	NORTH	EAST
1 NT	Pass	2 ♣	Pass
2 ♡	Pass	4 ♡	All Pass
			Opening lead — ◊ K

How the hand was played: West took his top diamonds and led a third diamond. Declarer discarded a club, cashed the ace of hearts and let the jack of hearts ride for a finesse.

This lost to the queen, much to South's annoyance. He could have saved the heart trick if he had guessed the hearts the other way.

West returned a trump, and South had to guess who held the queen of clubs. Using what he called his brain, South decided that both of the missing queens were not likely to be dealt to the same opponent. For this "reason" he finessed through East for the queen of clubs.

This finesse lost also, and South was down one. South is still screaming about his bad luck, but it would be a mistake to listen to him.

GOOD ODDS

The odds were better than 2 to 1 that the five missing trumps would be divided 3-2. If so, there was no need for South to guess about either queen.

South should take the second round of trumps with the king instead of letting the jack ride as a finesse. This leaves only the queen out against him.

Declarer runs the three spades and then leads a trump to give up a trick to the queen. Any return will then give him his contract.

A club return gives declarer a free finesse. Any other return allows dummy to ruff while South discards another club. Either way, the game is safe.

Enterprising Bidding Calls for Bold Play

One of my bridge friends bids like a bold, swashbuckling pirate and plays the cards like a rabbit. He is always surprised when this combination turns him into a dish of hasenpfeffer.

North dealer   **Both sides vulnerable**

NORTH-D
♠ K 8 6 2
♡ A K Q 5 3
♢ 9 6 5 3
♣ None

WEST	EAST
♠ 5 3	♠ 4
♡ 9 2	♡ J 10 8 4
♢ A K Q J 8 7 2	♢ 10 4
♣ K 7	♣ A Q J 10 9 3

SOUTH
♠ A Q J 10 9 7
♡ 7 6
♢ None
♣ 8 6 5 4 2

Defense Tricks:

☐ ☐ ☐ ☐ ☐ ☐ ☐ ☐ ☐ ☐ ☐ ☐ ☐

Bid the hand your way:

North	East	South	West
_____	_____	_____	_____
_____	_____	_____	_____
_____	_____	_____	_____
_____	_____	Opening Lead	_____

How the hand was bid:

NORTH	EAST	SOUTH	WEST
1 ♡	2 ♣	2 ♠	3 ◇
3 ♠	4 ♣	4 ◇	5 ♣
6 ♣	Pass	7 ♠	All Pass

Opening lead — ◇ K

How the hand was played: My friend ruffed the first diamond and drew two rounds of trumps. "Safety first," he burbled, not knowing he had already thrown his grand slam away.

South cashed the top hearts, ruffed a heart, ruffed a club in dummy and discarded on the last good heart. Declarer had played the first tricks quickly, but he made up for this by staring at the dummy for several minutes. The opponents were patient and they eventually got a trick.

HASTY PLAY

South can make the hand if he does his thinking early rather than late. He needs only normal breaks.

Declarer should ruff the first diamond with a high trump, lead a heart to dummy to ruff a second diamond with a high trump and should lead another heart to dummy to ruff a third diamond with a high trump. Next, South leads the seven of spades to dummy's eight and ruffs a fourth diamond.

Declarer ruffs a club in dummy, ruffs a low heart with his last trump, ruffs another club in dummy and draws the last trump with the king of spades. Only at the eleventh trick is it correct to draw the last trump!

Dummy takes the last two tricks with the ace of hearts and the last heart, which is good by this time.

If South had looked ahead he would have seen that his idea of a safe line of play made the grand slam depend on getting a 3-3 break in hearts. The correct play works also when the hearts break 4-2.

Mathematician Solves Problem of the Queen

When Ivar Stakgold is not winning national bridge championships he's busy spinning out long lines of logic as professor of mathematics at Northwestern University. Sometimes he spins out a long line at the bridge table.

West dealer   **Neither side vulnerable**

NORTH
♠ A 9
♡ A 8 4 3 2
♢ A 9 8 6
♣ Q 7

WEST-D   **EAST**
♠ K Q 10 8 5   ♠ J 7 4 3
♡ 9 5   ♡ Q 6
♢ Q 2   ♢ 10 7 3
♣ A K J 6   ♣ 10 5 3 2

SOUTH
♠ 6 2
♡ K J 10 7
♢ K J 5 4
♣ 9 8 4

Defense Tricks:

☐ ☐ ☐ ☐ ☐ ☐ ☐ ☐ ☐ ☐ ☐ ☐ ☐

Bid the hand your way:

North	East	South	West
_____	_____	_____	_____
_____	_____	_____	_____
_____	_____	_____	_____
_____	_____	_____	_____
		Opening Lead _____	

How the hand was bid:

WEST	NORTH	EAST	SOUTH
1 ♠	Double	2 ♠	3 ♡
3 ♠	4 ♡	All Pass	

Opening lead — ♣ K

How the hand was played: West cashed two high clubs and switched to the king of spades. Professor Stakgold took the ace of spades and returned the suit.

East looked at dummy's low spade doubtfully and after a long moment or two put up the jack. West took several seconds to consider and then overtook with the queen. West then led the jack of clubs for dummy to ruff.

NOTHING DELICIOUS

"Why did East step up with the jack of spades?" the Professor wondered. "He could not have had anything delicious to lead back, so why did he want to win the trick? He must have realized that his partner's natural switch would be to trumps, and this would worry East only if he had the queen of trumps."

This was one problem solved. Stakgold went on.

"But why did West overtake with the queen of spades? If his partner wanted to return a trump, West wasn't worried. But West was worried about a diamond return. Therefore West must have the queen of diamonds."

So the Professor cashed the ace of hearts, led another heart to pick up the queen and then led out the king and ace of diamonds to pick up West's queen.

The opponents stared at him in amazement and some resentment. "Why didn't you take a finesse?" they asked. "How did you work it out?"

Stakgold shrugged. "It was obvious," he said.

149

Standard Lead Is Not So Hot

A lifetime at the bridge table has taught me not to lead the highest card of three cards in partner's suit. From 8-6-2 of partner's suit I lead the deuce, not the eight.

North dealer   **Both sides vulnerable**

NORTH-D
♠ A 6 3
♡ 7 5
♦ A J 4
♣ K Q 10 9 6

WEST	EAST
♠ 8 7 4 2	♠ Q J 9
♡ Q 6 2	♡ A 10 9 8 4
♦ 7 3	♦ 10 9 8 6
♣ 8 7 3 2	♣ A

SOUTH
♠ K 10 5
♡ K J 3
♦ K Q 5 2
♣ J 5 4

Defense Tricks:

☐ ☐ ☐ ☐ ☐ ☐ ☐ ☐ ☐ ☐ ☐ ☐ ☐

Bid the hand your way:

North	East	South	West
_____	_____	_____	_____
_____	_____	_____	_____
_____	_____	_____	_____
_____	_____	_____	_____
		Opening Lead	_____

150

How the hand was bid:

NORTH	EAST	SOUTH	WEST
1 ♣	1 ♡	2 NT	Pass
3 NT	All Pass		

Opening lead — ♡ 2

How the hand was played: When this hand was played at a friend's house, West was a private banker, East was a publisher and the others were equally disreputable.

When West opened the deuce of hearts, he was clearly leading from four hearts or from three hearts headed by an honor. That's the way you expect a banker to lead.

East took the ace of hearts and returned the ten. Now South was sure that West had led the deuce from Q-x-x.

BLOCKS SUIT

South blocked the hearts by stepping up with the king at the second trick. He knocked out the ace of clubs, but then West had to win the next heart trick and abandon the suit. The defenders could get only two hearts and one club.

Now go back to the opening lead and see what happens if West is likely to be leading the deuce of hearts from x-x-x instead of Q-x-x. If East has the queen of hearts, South can make the contract only by finessing at the second trick. But if West has the queen, South must play the king of hearts at the second trick.

In this situation, South must guess what to do. He will often guess wrong because he does not know what the opening lead means.

When the actual play took place, South didn't have to guess. He had a sure thing.

I'm ornery about such matters. I prefer not to help my opponents. That's why I prefer to lead the lowest card from x-x-x of partner's suit.

Strong Trumps Need Protection

If you have time enough to hang around for the next ten thousand years you'll find out that little drops of water will wear away even the hardest rocks. The same sort of thing can happen to your trump suit, except that the process is quicker.

South dealer   **Both sides vulnerable**

NORTH

♠ 10 6
♡ Q J 2
◇ J 10 7 3
♣ K Q 9 2

WEST   EAST

♠ K 8 5 4 2   ♠ 7 3
♡ 5   ♡ 9 8 7 4
◇ Q 9 6 4 2   ◇ A 8 5
♣ 6 5   ♣ A 10 8 7

SOUTH-D

♠ A Q J 9
♡ A K 10 6 3
◇ K
♣ J 4 3

Defense Tricks:

☐ ☐ ☐ ☐ ☐ ☐ ☐ ☐ ☐ ☐ ☐ ☐ ☐

Bid the hand your way:

North	East	South	West
———	———	———	———
———	———	———	———
———	———	———	———
———	———	———	———
		Opening Lead	———

152

How the hand was bid:

SOUTH	WEST	NORTH	EAST
1 ♡	Pass	2 ♡	Pass
4 ♡	All Pass		

Opening lead — ◊ 4

How the hand was played: East won the first trick with the ace of diamonds and returned a diamond. South ruffed, never dreaming that his solid trump suit would suffer.

Declarer led the ace of trumps and continued with a trump to dummy's jack, discovering the bad trump break. He next led the ten of spades from dummy for a finesse.

West won with the king of spades and boldly returned the queen of diamonds, forcing South to ruff again. The erosion left South with only one trump in his hand and one trump in dummy, while East had two trumps.

CLEARS TRUMPS

Sooner or later South had to lead a club, and East took the ace of clubs and cleared trumps by returning a heart. This left East with the only remaining trump, which eventually took the setting trick.

South can get out of the way of those little drops of water if he doesn't ruff at the second trick. South should discard a spade, allowing West to win with the queen of diamonds. Declarer can later discard two more spades on dummy's jack and ten of diamonds, thus avoiding the loss of a spade trick in exchange for the diamond trick he has given up.

No matter what West returns, South can draw trumps and get back to dummy with a club to take his spade discards on the good diamonds.

Best Finesse Is No Finesse

"How should I have played that hand?" South asked after putting up a pretty poor exhibition. His partner gave him the time-honored answer: "Under an assumed name."

South dealer   **Both sides vulnerable**

NORTH
♠ K 5 2
♡ 10 9 3 2
♢ 5 4 2
♣ A J 6

WEST   EAST
♠ Q J 10   ♠ A 9 8 6 4
♡ 8   ♡ J 5
♢ K 10 6   ♢ J 9 8 7
♣ 10 9 5 4 3 2   ♣ Q 8

SOUTH-D
♠ 7 3
♡ A K Q 7 6 4
♢ A Q 3
♣ K 7

Defense Tricks:

☐ ☐ ☐ ☐ ☐ ☐ ☐ ☐ ☐ ☐ ☐ ☐ ☐

Bid the hand your way:

North	East	South	West
_____	_____	_____	_____
_____	_____	_____	_____
_____	_____	_____	_____
_____	_____	_____	_____
		Opening Lead	_____

154

How the hand was bid:

SOUTH	WEST	NORTH	EAST
1 ♡	Pass	2 ♡	Pass
4 ♡	All Pass		

Opening lead — ♠ Q

How the hand was played: South ruffed the third round of spades, drew two high trumps and led a low trump to dummy. Then he tried the diamond finesse, losing to the king.

Back came a diamond to the ace, and South cashed the king of clubs and tried the club finesse in desperation. East took the queen of clubs and a diamond trick, collecting 200 points.

North shook his head dolefully. "If you played the hand double-dummy," he suggested, "you could lose another trick."

BEST PLAY

The best play makes the contract. After drawing two trumps, South cashes the king and ace of clubs and throws a diamond on the jack of clubs. Since the queen of clubs has dropped in the meantime, the contract is now assured.

If the queen of clubs hasn't dropped, an opponent will win the third club trick. If West wins (which means that the club finesse would have worked), he must return a diamond up to the ace-queen. (A club return would let dummy ruff while South discarded the queen of diamonds.)

If East has started with thee or more clubs to the queen and plays the queen on dummy's jack, South ruffs, plays the ace of diamonds and leads a low trump to return a diamond.

South therefore makes the contract whenever West has the queen of clubs, if East has the doubleton queen, and also whenever East has the king of diamonds, or if West has the singleton or doubleton king of diamonds.

Disregard Danger to Save Life

No sensible person makes it a habit to jump out of windows, but it may be the right way to get out if the building is on fire. The same sort of thing may happen in a bridge hand.

North dealer   **North-South vulnerable**

NORTH-D
♠ 8 7 3
♡ K 6
♦ A K Q J 7 6
♣ A K

WEST   **EAST**
♠ A 6 2   ♠ 5 4
♡ Q J 10 5   ♡ A 9 8 2
♦ 10   ♦ 9 5 4 2
♣ J 9 6 3 2   ♣ 8 7 5

SOUTH
♠ K Q J 10 9
♡ 7 4 3
♦ 8 3
♣ Q 10 4

Defense Tricks:

☐ ☐ ☐ ☐ ☐ ☐ ☐ ☐ ☐ ☐ ☐ ☐ ☐

Bid the hand your way:

North	East	South	West
_____	_____	_____	_____
_____	_____	_____	_____
_____	_____	_____	_____
_____	_____	_____	_____

Opening Lead _____

How the hand was bid:

NORTH	EAST	SOUTH	WEST
2 ◊	Pass	2 NT	Pass
3 NT	Pass	4 ♠	All Pass

Opening lead — ♡ Q

How the hand was played: The defenders led three rounds of hearts, forcing declarer to ruff in dummy.

Declarer led a spade from dummy and played the king of spades from his hand, hoping to lure out the ace. No such luck; West calmly played a low spade on this trick.

South continued with another spade, and this time West took his ace. South held his breath, hoping for a heart return. This would allow declarer to ruff and draw the last trump.

LOCKED IN DUMMY

West had a better idea. He returned a club, and now South was locked in the dummy. There were only clubs and diamonds in the dummy, and when declarer led the second diamond, West defeated the contract by ruffing.

South should have seen what sort of defense was in store for him. When the first trump trick was refused, South should have done what he could to find a way out—however dangerous.

After winning the first trump trick with the king, South should cash dummy's top clubs and then continue with one high diamond. Then he can lead another trump to force out the ace.

Now the defenders cannot lock him in dummy. South easily wins a club or heart return. If the player with the ace of trumps can lead a second round of diamonds, dummy wins. Declarer then ruffs a diamond and draws trumps safely.

Short Trump Suit Calls for Caution

Good bidders try to find a trump suit in which the partnership has a safe majority. It is far more difficult to keep control when you hold only seven trumps and the opponents have six, but you must sometimes take this risk.

East dealer   **North-South vulnerable**

NORTH
♠ K 7 4
♡ Q 10 8 5 3
◇ Q 7
♣ 10 6 5

WEST
♠ J 10 8 5
♡ 7 4 2
◇ 9 4
♣ J 9 4 2

EAST-D
♠ 9 2
♡ K J 9 6
◇ 8 5 2
♣ A K Q 7

SOUTH
♠ A Q 6 3
♡ A
◇ A K J 10 6 3
♣ 8 3

Defense Tricks:

☐ ☐ ☐ ☐ ☐ ☐ ☐ ☐ ☐ ☐ ☐ ☐ ☐

Bid the hand your way:

North	East	South	West
___	___	___	___
___	___	___	___
___	___	___	___
___	___	___	___
		Opening Lead ___	

How the hand was bid:

EAST	SOUTH	WEST	NORTH
1 ♣	Double	Pass	1 ♡
Pass	2 ◇	Pass	2 ♡
Pass	2 ♠	Pass	3 ♠
Pass	4 ♠	All Pass	

Opening lead — ♣ 2

How the hand was played: South had a safe diamond suit but could not win eleven tricks at diamonds. He decided to try for ten tricks at spades despite the trump shortness.

The defenders took their two clubs and continued with a third club, forcing South to ruff. Declarer could not afford to discard on the third club since he would then have to lose the setting trick to a trump.

South continued with the king and ace of trumps. This left a small trump in dummy and the queen in South's hand, with two trumps still out. If South tried to draw the two trumps with his queen, West would eventually get a trick with his last trump and another with his last club.

LEAVES TRUMPS OUT

Actually, South was willing to leave the last two trumps out. He began to run the diamonds, allowing the defenders to ruff.

West ruffed the third diamond but could not defeat the contract. If he returned a club, dummy could ruff—and this was South's reason for leaving a trump in dummy. South could then get back to his hand with the ace of hearts to draw the last trump and run the rest of the diamonds.

It would do West no good to discard hearts instead of ruffing. South would just continue to run his diamonds and wasn't particular which ten tricks he took.

Too Much Wealth Burdens Declarer

The trouble with many of us is that we have it too soft. We have so much more than we need that we're worse off than if we had less. As usual, I have a bridge hand to illustrate the sermon.

West dealer   **East-West vulnerable**

NORTH

♠ 9 5 4
♡ 10 4 3
◇ Q 6 5 4 2
♣ 8 7

WEST-D   **EAST**

♠ 8 7 3 2   ♠ K Q J 10 6
♡ 8 7 5   ♡ 9
◇ A 3   ◇ K J 9 8
♣ K J 9 6   ♣ 10 4 2

SOUTH

♠ A
♡ A K Q J 6 2
◇ 10 7
♣ A Q 5 3

Defense Tricks:

☐ ☐ ☐ ☐ ☐ ☐ ☐ ☐ ☐ ☐ ☐ ☐ ☐

Bid the hand your way:

North	East	South	West
_____	_____	_____	_____
_____	_____	_____	_____
_____	_____	_____	_____
		Opening Lead	_____

How the hand was bid:

WEST	NORTH	EAST	SOUTH
Pass	Pass	1 ♠	Double
3 ♠	Pass	Pass	4 ♡
All Pass			

Opening lead — ◊ A

How the hand was played: West opened the ace of diamonds and led another diamond to East's jack. East returned a low diamond, and South ruffed with the ace of trumps to make sure of shutting West out.

South wanted to take a club finesse, so he led the deuce of trumps to dummy's ten and returned a club to finesse with the queen. West won the king of clubs and returned a trump, whereupon South began to see the error of his ways.

ONLY ONE RUFF

Only one trump was left in dummy, so South could ruff only one club in dummy. Consequently, South had to lose a second club trick. Down one.

South would have made his contract if he had held the deuce of clubs instead of the queen. His hand would not have looked so strong, but he would have been free from temptation.

After trumping the third round of diamonds, South should plan to ruff two clubs in dummy—one with a low trump and the other with the ten of trumps. He doesn't need a club finesse, but he does need two trumps in dummy.

The best plan is to lead a low club immediately. If a spade is returned (as good a defense as any), South takes the ace of spades, cashes the ace of clubs and ruffs a club in dummy. He returns by ruffing a spade, ruffs his last club with dummy's ten of hearts and leads a trump to draw the rest of the trumps.

You Need Two Trumps to Ruff Two Losers

In certain difficult hands you need a little luck to make your contract. Don't ask for more luck than you really need or you'll wear out your rabbit's foot.

South dealer   Neither side vulnerable

NORTH
♠ K Q 5 4
♡ K Q 9 3
♢ 8 3
♣ K 7 3

WEST
♠ J 10 8 7
♡ J 7 4
♢ 10 5 4
♣ Q J 10

EAST
♠ A 9 3
♡ 2
♢ Q J 9 6
♣ A 9 8 5 2

SOUTH-D
♠ 6 2
♡ A 10 8 6 5
♢ A K 7 2
♣ 6 4

Defense Tricks:

☐ ☐ ☐ ☐ ☐ ☐ ☐ ☐ ☐ ☐ ☐ ☐ ☐ ☐

Bid the hand your way:

North	East	South	West
_____	_____	_____	_____
_____	_____	_____	_____
_____	_____	_____	_____
_____	_____	_____	_____
		Opening Lead	_____

SOUTH	WEST	NORTH	EAST
1 ♡	Pass	3 ♡	Pass
4 ♡	All Pass		

Opening lead — ♣ Q

How the hand was played: South ruffed the third round of clubs and drew three rounds of trumps. This was pure foolishness, as he soon discovered.

South next led a spade, losing the king to the ace. Now South needed the rest of the tricks, with only one trump in dummy to take care of two losing diamonds.

South would have made the contract if the four missing trumps had broken 2-2 since then he could have saved two trumps in dummy for the losing diamonds. He would have been safe if West had held the ace of spades since then he could have discarded a diamond on one of dummy's high spades. Still, he asked more of luck than he really needed.

LEAD SPADES EARLY

After ruffing the third club, South should lead a spade at once. If West has the ace of spades, it can do no harm to find out the good news at once.

Actually, East would take the ace of spades and return a diamond to the ace. Now South should draw one round of trumps with the king since he is safe if the jack happens to drop. When only small trumps appear, South should start a crossruff without drawing the rest of the trumps.

The idea is to cash the queen of spades and the king of diamonds and then ruff two diamonds in dummy or two spades in the South hand. This will be perfectly safe if West has length in spades or if East has length in diamonds. Even if the wrong opponent is long in spades or diamonds, the worst that can happen is that declarer will have to ruff with dummy's nine or his own ten and hope that the next player cannot overruff with the jack.

Lucky Player Picks Right Partner

If you want to be lucky at bridge, pick a partner who weighs one hundred and twenty pounds ringside, is scared of his own shadow and can't think quickly enough about a bridge hand to complain about your bidding or play. Of course you can't win with such a partner but you'll be lucky enough to survive if you lose finesses that you shouldn't have taken.

South dealer   **Both sides vulnerable**

NORTH

♠ A 8 7 4
♡ A 10 5 3
♦ K 7
♣ A J 4

WEST   EAST

♠ 5 2   ♠ Q J 10 9 6
♡ 9 8 6   ♡ Q 2
♦ Q 10 5 4   ♦ J 6 2
♣ 10 9 8 6   ♣ 5 3 2

SOUTH-D

♠ K 3
♡ K J 7 4
♦ A 9 8 3
♣ K Q 7

Defense Tricks:

☐ ☐ ☐ ☐ ☐ ☐ ☐ ☐ ☐ ☐ ☐ ☐ ☐ ☐ ☐

Bid the hand your way:

North	East	South	West

Opening Lead _____

How the hand was bid:

SOUTH	WEST	NORTH	EAST
1 NT	Pass	2 ♣	Pass
2 ♡	Pass	6 ♡	All Pass
			Opening lead — ♣ 10

How the hand was played: South won the first trick with the king of clubs, cashed the king of hearts and then tried a finesse with dummy's ten of hearts. He felt very unlucky when he lost this finesse; after all, the finesse would have worked if West had held the queen of hearts.

East returned the queen of spades, and South had another chance to make the slam. He could ruff two diamonds in the dummy and then get back to his hand to draw the last trump; or he could ruff two spades in his own hand and then get back to dummy to draw the last trump. Which plan to adopt?

South didn't know which opponent had the last trump or how spades and diamonds would break. After tossing a mental coin, he played the spades and allowed West to overruff. Down one.

UNLUCKY AGAIN

South complained that he was unlucky again. He would have been safe if East had held the last trump or if West had held four spades. He would have made the slam if he had played the diamonds instead of the spades.

South's real bad luck was that he had a partner who was not afraid to speak up. North had a small vocabulary, but it was very active, and he managed to point out that South deserved everything that happened to him for taking a trump finesse.

The correct play is to draw two rounds of trumps with the ace and king. If the queen is still out, South can ruff spades or diamonds or both. All he can lose is one trump trick.

Greedy Player May Lose Slam

When you're playing a comfortable slam contract, look around carefully for a way to lose a trick. You don't want to give up just any old trick, but you're eager to give up one that will cinch the contract for you.

North dealer   **North-South vulnerable**

NORTH-D
♠ K Q 9 5 2
♡ 8 3
◇ 6 5 3
♣ A 6 3

WEST   **EAST**
♠ J 10 8 4   ♠ 7
♡ 7 4   ♡ 10 6 2
◇ K 8 2   ◇ Q 10 9 4
♣ J 10 9 5   ♣ K 8 7 4 2

SOUTH
♠ A 6 3
♡ A K Q J 9 5
◇ A J 7
♣ Q

Defense Tricks:

☐ ☐ ☐ ☐ ☐ ☐ ☐ ☐ ☐ ☐ ☐ ☐ ☐

Bid the hand your way:

North	East	South	West
_____	_____	_____	_____
_____	_____	_____	_____
_____	_____	_____	_____
_____	_____	_____	_____
		Opening Lead	_____

How the hand was bid:

NORTH	EAST	SOUTH	WEST
Pass	Pass	2 ♡	Pass
2 ♠	Pass	4 NT	Pass
5 ◇	Pass	5 NT	Pass
6 ◇	Pass	6 ♡	All Pass

Opening lead — ♣ J

How the hand was played: Declarer wins the opening lead in dummy with the ace of clubs and draws three rounds of trumps. It is then time to work on the spades.

South needs precisely four spade tricks to make the slam. A fifth spade trick is quite unimportant.

South should begin the spades by taking the ace. Then he leads a low spade toward dummy. West casually plays the eight of spades since he would force declarer to play the spades correctly if he put up the ten or jack of spades.

MUST FINESSE

When West plays the eight of spades, declarer must take a deep finesse with dummy's nine of spades. Win or lose, this guarantees the slam.

As the cards lie, East is out of spades, and the deep finesse wins. The rest of the spades are good, and South wins all thirteen tricks.

South wouldn't mind losing the deep finesse. If East were able to play the ten or jack of spades, the suit would break 3-2. Then the rest of dummy's spades would be good and South would discard his two low diamonds on dummy's last two spades.

As the cards lie, the deep finesse is necessary to make the slam. If South makes the mistake of winning the second spade trick with dummy's king or queen, he cannot develop four spade tricks. South eventually loses two diamonds and is down one.

Don't Postpone Your End Play

Forcing an opponent to help you is often called an "end play," because it usually takes place near the end of the hand. Keep your ears open in case opportunity knocks earlier.

West dealer   **East-West vulnerable**

NORTH
- ♠ A 8
- ♡ A J 7 3
- ◊ 8 5 3
- ♣ 9 7 5 2

WEST-D   **EAST**
- ♠ Q 10 3   - ♠ None
- ♡ K Q 10 9   - ♡ 8 6 4 2
- ◊ A Q 9   - ◊ J 10 6 4 2
- ♣ K 8 3   - ♣ J 10 6 4

SOUTH
- ♠ K J 9 7 6 5 4 2
- ♡ 5
- ◊ K 7
- ♣ A Q

Defense Tricks:

☐ ☐ ☐ ☐ ☐ ☐ ☐ ☐ ☐ ☐ ☐ ☐

Bid the hand your way:

North	East	South	West
_____	_____	_____	_____
_____	_____	_____	_____
_____	_____	_____	_____
_____	_____	_____	_____
		Opening Lead	_____

How the hand was bid:

WEST	NORTH	EAST	SOUTH
1 NT	Pass	2 ◇	2 ♠
Pass	3 ♠	Pass	4 ♠
All Pass			

Opening lead — ♡ K

How the hand was played: Declarer won the first trick with the ace of hearts, ruffed a heart and led a trump to the ace. The bad trump break produced a smile from West and a naughty word from South.

Declarer took the king of spades and gave West his trump trick, whereupon West got out safely by leading the queen of hearts. South ruffed and led out the rest of his trumps.

West threw away his hearts, a club and the queen of diamonds.

GOES WRONG

The clever diamond discard led South astray. He had a diamond, thinking that West would have to win and return clubs up to the ace-queen. Instead, East overtook the nine of diamonds with the ten and led a club through South.

Declarer had to lose a club trick as well as another diamond. Down one.

South could have led the ace and queen of clubs, forcing West to win and lead diamonds to the king, but South was hoodwinked by a very pretty discard. South waited too long for his end play; he was asleep at the first trick.

Declarer should allow West to win the first trick with the king of hearts. What can West do to keep out of trouble?

If West continues with a low heart, declarer wins a finesse with dummy's jack. If West leads anything else, South gets a free finesse.

Don't Take Risks If You Can't Gain

Are you suspicious when an opponent catches a singleton king? Instead of clutching your cards closer to the vest, see if you can follow your opponent's reasoning.

North dealer   **Both sides vulnerable**

NORTH-D

♠ A Q 6 4
♡ 6 5 3
◇ A Q 7 6 3
♣ A

WEST	EAST
♠ 8 5 3	♠ 9 7
♡ A Q 10	♡ 8 7 4 2
◇ 8 4	◇ K
♣ Q J 10 7 4	♣ K 9 8 5 3 2

SOUTH

♠ K J 10 2
♡ K J 9
◇ J 10 9 5 2
♣ 6

Defense Tricks:

☐ ☐ ☐ ☐ ☐ ☐ ☐ ☐ ☐ ☐ ☐ ☐

Bid the hand your way:

North	East	South	West
_____	_____	_____	_____
_____	_____	_____	_____
_____	_____	_____	_____
_____	_____	_____	_____

Opening Lead _____

How the hand was bid:

NORTH	EAST	SOUTH	WEST
1 ◇	Pass	1 ♠	Pass
3 ♠	Pass	4 ♠	All Pass
			Opening lead — ♣ Q

How the hand was played: When this hand was played in a recent rubber bridge game, declarer took the club opening and drew three rounds of trumps, ending in his hand. He then led the jack of diamonds.

West played the four of diamonds, and declarer immediately put up dummy's ace. East dropped the king and shrank back into his chair. "One peek is worth two finesses," he growled.

Actually, South hadn't peeked. He knew that he might lose the contract if he finessed; he couldn't go down if he played dummy's ace of diamonds.

DANGEROUS FINESSE

If South finesses and loses to the king, back comes a heart. South loses his heart play, whatever it may be, and West gets out safely with a low diamond. Sooner or later declarer must try another heart play and thus loses three hearts and a diamond. Hence finessing may cost South the contract.

Suppose declarer catches only low diamonds with dummy's ace. He gives up a diamond and back comes a heart. The opponents can take two heart tricks but must either set up a heart trick for South or give him a ruff-discard by returning a club. South must make his game.

Even if West has all three of the missing diamonds, South is still safe. He gives up a diamond, wins the third diamond in dummy and leads a heart. West can get only two heart tricks but must then return a heart or a club to give declarer his tenth trick.

Read about Bridge to Know Best Play

One advantage of reading about bridge is that you can be ready
with the right play without having to think for twenty minutes at
the table. The difference showed up when this hand was played.

NORTH-D
- ♠ J 6
- ♡ 6 3
- ◇ A K J 8 5
- ♣ A 10 4 2

WEST
- ♠ Q 10
- ♡ A K 9 4 2
- ◇ 10 7 3
- ♣ 8 7 3

EAST
- ♠ K 8 4
- ♡ 8 7 5
- ◇ Q 9 6 4
- ♣ 9 6 5

SOUTH
- ♠ A 9 7 5 3 2
- ♡ Q J 10
- ◇ 2
- ♣ K Q J

Defense Tricks:

☐ ☐ ☐ ☐ ☐ ☐ ☐ ☐ ☐ ☐ ☐ ☐ ☐

Bid the hand your way:

North	East	South	West
_____	_____	_____	_____
_____	_____	_____	_____
_____	_____	_____	_____
		Opening Lead _____	

How the hand was bid:

NORTH	EAST	SOUTH	WEST
1 ♢	Pass	1 ♠	Pass
2 ♣	Pass	3 ♠	Pass
4 ♠	All Pass		

Opening lead — ♡ K

How the hand was played: West led three rounds of hearts, and South won the third with the queen. South, a self-taught player, then wondered how to limit the trump loss to one trick.

If you have ever been in this position you know that one minute seems very long and that three minutes seems about twice as long as eternity. After about two minutes of thought, South was too embarrassed to take any more time. He led a diamond to dummy and returned the jack of spades.

East was much too experienced to cover dummy's jack with the king of spades. South's bidding indicated at least a six-card trump suit, so West could have only one or two spades at most. A cover would help South, but could not help the defenders.

LOSES TWO TRUMPS

After this play, South had to lose two trump tricks, and his contract. He could have found the right line of play if he had really thought for twenty minutes or if he had spent five minutes a day reading a bridge column or book.

South can make the contract only if West has Q-10 or K-10 of trumps. Declarer starts by leading a low trump from his hand.

West must step up with his picture card, winning the trick. Declarer later gets to dummy with a diamond to lead the jack of spades for a finesse through East. This captures the ten and the other picture card at the same time.

173

Sensible Player Says Right Thing

No sensible man claims that he understands women; it might get back to his wife. All men can do is compare notes, and this hand is presented as a service to male bridge players.

North dealer   **Both sides vulnerable**

NORTH-D
♠ A 8 7 6 3
♡ K 9 3
♢ K 3 2
♣ A 7

WEST	EAST
♠ K J 5 2	♠ Q 10 9 4
♡ 4	♡ J 10 8 6
♢ Q J 10 9	♢ A 8 7 5
♣ J 10 8 3	♣ 9

SOUTH
♠ None
♡ A Q 7 5 2
♢ 6 4
♣ K Q 6 5 4 2

Defense Tricks:

☐ ☐ ☐ ☐ ☐ ☐ ☐ ☐ ☐ ☐ ☐ ☐ ☐

Bid the hand your way:

North	East	South	West
_____	_____	_____	_____
_____	_____	_____	_____
_____	_____	_____	_____
_____	_____	_____	_____
		Opening Lead	_____

How the hand was bid:

NORTH	EAST	SOUTH	WEST
1 ♠	Pass	2 ♡	Pass
3 ♡	Pass	4 ♣	Pass
4 ♡	All Pass		

Opening lead — ◊ Q

How the hand was played: West opened the queen of diamonds and continued the suit until South ruffed. Declarer drew two rounds of trumps with the king and ace, followed by a club to the ace and another back to the king.

South ruffed a low club in dummy, and East again discarded. Now South had to waste a trump to get back to her own hand.

East ruffed the next club and led a diamond to force out South's last trump. East still had a trump for the setting trick.

South pounced on her partner. "You told me the odds were more than 2 to 1 against a 4-1 break. They must be 10 to 1 against the break I just got. Why do you hide the truth from me.?"

SCRAMBLES OUT

"You're exactly right about the odds," North said. "You're a beautiful mathematician." And he put enough accent on the "beautiful" to scramble out of the hot water.

North might have pointed out that South should draw only one round of trumps, with dummy's king. Then she takes two top clubs and ruffs a club. East discards, but dummy still has a trump to lead to the South hand. Declarer takes the ace and queen of trumps and then leads clubs until East uses up his last trump. South makes the rest with her own last trump and good clubs.

Why didn't North say so? I was North, and I've been married too long to go looking for trouble.

Expert Guesses Only If Necessary

Since an expert knows more about the hand and more about the players, he guesses right about 20 percent more often than the average player. The expert's biggest advantage is that he doesn't try to guess when he has a sure thing.

South dealer   **North-South vulnerable**

```
                    NORTH
                    ♠ 5 2
                    ♡ K 7 6 5
                    ◇ Q J 5 3
                    ♣ 8 7 3

        WEST                        EAST
        ♠ Q 8 7 4                   ♠ K 10 9 6 3
        ♡ J 10 9                    ♡ Q
        ◇ 7 6                       ◇ 9 8 2
        ♣ Q 10 4 2                  ♣ A 9 6 5

                    SOUTH-D
                    ♠ A J
                    ♡ A 8 4 3 2
                    ◇ A K 10 4
                    ♣ K J
```

Defense Tricks:

☐ ☐ ☐ ☐ ☐ ☐ ☐ ☐ ☐ ☐ ☐ ☐ ☐

Bid the hand your way:

North	East	South	West
_____	_____	_____	_____
_____	_____	_____	_____
_____	_____	_____	_____

Opening Lead _____

176

How the hand was bid:

SOUTH	WEST	NORTH	EAST
1 ♡	Pass	2 ♡	Pass
4 ♡	All Pass		

Opening lead — ♡ J

How the hand was played: West opened the jack of hearts, and declarer took the top hearts and gave up a heart. West returned a diamond, and declarer took three rounds of diamonds, cashed the ace of spades and gave up a spade.

East won with the king of spades and returned a low club through South's K-J. South's contract now depended on whether he guessed the right play.

If you weren't looking at all the cards, you might play the jack of clubs about three times out of ten.

There's nothing to be ashamed of if you guess right about seven times out of ten. The only thing to be ashamed of is guessing at all when you should make a sure thing out of this hand.

START SPADES

The correct play is to win the first trick in dummy with the king of hearts and return a low spade at once. You intend to play the jack from your hand to lose the spade trick to West. East cannot really prevent you from doing so.

West leads another trump. You win, cash the ace of spades, run the diamonds and put West in with a trump.

West has only spades and clubs. If he returns a spade, you ruff in dummy and discard the jack of clubs. If West returns a club, you have no problem.

Whenever possible force the safe opponent to lead a suit in which you have to guess. Keep the dangerous opponent out of the lead. In this case, shut East out and force West to lead clubs for you.

Don't Listen to Table Talk

We all know that people shouldn't talk during the bidding or play of a bridge hand, but we also know that they sometimes do. Fortunately, this table talk doesn't seem to help the chief offenders.

North dealer   **North-South vulnerable**

NORTH-D

♠ 6 4 2
♡ A Q 6
♢ K Q 3 2
♣ K 7 6

WEST   EAST

♠ 9 8 7   ♠ 5 3
♡ 8 7 4 3   ♡ 10 5 2
♢ A J 10 7   ♢ 8 6 5 4
♣ J 4   ♣ Q 10 9 8

SOUTH

♠ A K Q J 10
♡ K J 9
♢ 9
♣ A 5 3 2

Defense Tricks:

☐ ☐ ☐ ☐ ☐ ☐ ☐ ☐ ☐ ☐ ☐ ☐ ☐

Bid the hand your way:

North	East	South	West
_____	_____	_____	_____
_____	_____	_____	_____
	_____	_____	_____

Opening Lead _____

How the hand was bid:

NORTH	EAST	SOUTH	WEST
1 ◇	Pass	2 ♠	Pass
2 NT	Pass	4 NT	Pass
5 ◇	Pass	6 ♠	All Pass

Opening lead — ♠ 9

How the hand was played: West opened the nine of spades, and South won with the ten. Declarer continued with two more rounds of trumps and then led the nine of diamonds.

"Is that a singleton?" West asked, looking suspiciously at the unoffending card. "If it is, I'm going to grab my trick."

"I cannot tell a lie," South replied. "That is my only diamond."

Nobody can censure South for this statement. He didn't start the conversation, and what he said was the simple truth.

TAKES ACE

West believed South, and took the ace of diamonds. Now there was no way to defeat the contract. South could eventually throw two clubs on dummy's king and queen of diamonds.

Strangely enough, West could defeat the contract only if South had a singleton diamond. But West would have to give up his diamond trick by playing the ten or jack of diamonds instead of the ace.

Dummy would win with the queen of diamonds, but then there would be no second diamond trick for declarer. He would eventually lose two club tricks to East.

It isn't always wise to grab your ace when declarer leads a singleton through you. Moreover, if you're informal enough to chatter while a hand is going on, don't use correct information to make the wrong play.

Timely Finesse May Save Life

"You are always writing harsh things about finesses," a read
complains. "Surely you can find something nice to say, if or
to please those of us who have always regarded the finesse as
friend."

South dealer Neither side vulnerab

NORTH

♠ K Q 4 3 2
♡ 5 3 2
◊ A 6
♣ 7 6 4

WEST EAST

♠ 9 8 7 5 ♠ A J 10
♡ None ♡ Q 10 9
◊ Q J 10 9 2 ◊ K 8 7 4
♣ Q 9 8 3 ♣ J 10 2

SOUTH-D

♠ 6
♡ A K J 8 7 6 4
◊ 5 3
♣ A K 5

Defense Tricks:

☐ ☐ ☐ ☐ ☐ ☐ ☐ ☐ ☐ ☐ ☐ ☐ ☐

Bid the hand your way:

North	East	South	West
_____	_____	_____	_____
_____	_____	_____	_____
_____	_____	_____	_____
_____	_____	_____	_____

Opening Lead _____

How the hand was bid:

SOUTH	WEST	NORTH	EAST
1 ♡	Pass	1 ♠	Pass
3 ♡	Pass	4 ♡	All Pass

Opening lead — ◇ Q

How the hand was played: Glad to oblige. In fact, this may be the right time to tell of the finesse that saved my life.

Don't ask where and when it all occurred. It's all mixed up in my mind with a tournament and a late meal that consisted largely of Welsh rabbit. But there I was, playing as the partner of a cannibal chief.

I had failed to make my previous contract, and the chief was scolding me when this hand appeared. "Just go down this time," he warned me, "and into the stewpot you go."

DESPERATE PLAY

I won the first trick in dummy with the ace of diamonds and led the deuce of hearts. East played the ten, and I took a desperate finesse with the jack of hearts.

West discarded a diamond, so I spread my hand and announced I was going to draw two more top trumps and run my ten tricks.

East, a vampire by the name of Dracula, was very annoyed at my finesse. "Just for peeking at my hand," he announced, "I'm going to take all your blood."

The cannibal chief came to my defense, and in the confusion I woke up. But I wrote the cards down with a shaking hand as a service to all my readers.

The immediate heart finesse was sure to keep me out of the stewpot. If the finesse worked, well and good. If it lost, the trumps would split 2-1, and I would eventually be able to lead the four of hearts to dummy's five and discard a losing club on a good spade.

181

Broth of a Player Finds Right Plan

Now I must tell you how it was with this tournament in Ireland, and let you be reading it with care for the great lesson there is in it. For in the matter of finesses you will be seeing that there's more than one road to cook a potato.

South dealer   **Neither side vulnerable**

NORTH
- ♠ A
- ♡ A J 9 8 6 2
- ♢ 5 4
- ♣ J 10 6 3

WEST
- ♠ Q 8 4
- ♡ K 4 3
- ♢ K J 10 7 3
- ♣ K 8

EAST
- ♠ K 10 9 7 5 3
- ♡ Q 10
- ♢ Q 9 8 2
- ♣ 5

SOUTH-D
- ♠ J 6 2
- ♡ 7 5
- ♢ A 6
- ♣ A Q 9 7 4 2

Defense Tricks:

☐ ☐ ☐ ☐ ☐ ☐ ☐ ☐ ☐ ☐ ☐ ☐ ☐ ☐

Bid the hand your way:

North	East	South	West
_____	_____	_____	_____
_____	_____	_____	_____
_____	_____	_____	_____
_____	_____	_____	_____

Opening Lead _____

How the hand was bid:

SOUTH	WEST	NORTH	EAST
1 ♣	1 ◇	1 ♡	1 ♠
2 ♣	2 ♠	4 ♣	4 ◇
5 ♣	All Pass		

Opening lead — ♠ 4

How the hand was played: We will not be singing songs, mark you, about the opening lead. At both tables of the match West led the four of spades.

The first declarer was after taking the club finesse, and the king of clubs in the West hand all the time. West took the club king and led back a diamond, and now the defenders could be taking a diamond trick whenever South gave them a heart. Ouch! Down one.

HIMSELF MAKES CONTRACT

Now I'm wanting to tell you how it was at the second table, and E. O. Barry playing the South cards. Himself won the first trick in dummy with the ace of spades, and next the broth of a lad led a club to the ace. Divil a bit of a finesse.

Barry ducked a heart to East's ten, won the diamond return with the ace, led a heart to the ace and ruffed a heart. Then Barry got to dummy by ruffing a spade and led an established heart to get rid of the losing diamond.

Our broth of a lad lost only one trump trick and one heart.

Barry's plan was better than a simple club finesse. First, the club king might drop under the ace. Second, setting up the hearts would almost surely work if East had the king of clubs, so that refusing the club finesse would cost nothing. Third, playing for the hearts would work even if West had the king of clubs if West had the doubleton K-Q of hearts or any three or four hearts.

A credit to the ould sod is this lad Barry.

Lead Right Card to Develop Suit

It's usually easy to pick the right suit to lead. Choosing the right card is not always quite as easy.

South dealer   **Neither side vulnerable**

NORTH

♠ A Q 10
♡ K 8 2
◇ K 10 9 8 4
♣ J 7

WEST	EAST
♠ 9 8 5	♠ 7 6 3 2
♡ Q 5 4	♡ J 9 7 6
◇ A 6 3	◇ Q 7 2
♣ 10 8 4 3	♣ A 5

SOUTH-D

♠ K J 4
♡ A 10 3
◇ J 5
♣ K Q 9 6 2

Defense Tricks:

☐ ☐ ☐ ☐ ☐ ☐ ☐ ☐ ☐ ☐ ☐ ☐ ☐

Bid the hand your way:

North	East	South	West
_____	_____	_____	_____
_____	_____	_____	_____
_____	_____	_____	_____
_____	_____	_____	_____
		Opening Lead	_____

184

How the hand was bid:

SOUTH	WEST	NORTH	WEST
1 ♣	Pass	1 ◇	Pass
1 NT	Pass	3 NT	All Pass

Opening lead — ♠ 9

How the hand was played: West led the nine of spades, and South overtook with the jack to win the trick in his own hand. Declarer returned the jack of diamonds for a finesse, losing to East's queen.

This put it squarely up to East. What should he return?

East could see that spades and diamonds were hopeless. South clearly had a real club suit since he would have been glad to bid one heart or one spade at his second turn if he had held a four-card major.

Hence East knew he had to lead a heart if he wanted to defeat the contract. But which heart?

East actually returned his fourth-best heart, the six. South played low, and West had to put up the queen to force out dummy's king. This left South with the A-10 of hearts over East's jack, and there was no further hope for the defense.

WRONG CARD

East led the wrong card. The correct return is the nine of hearts.

If South plays low, the nine is high enough to drive out dummy's king. When West gets in with the ace of diamonds, he can return the queen of hearts to set up two heart tricks for East. South must lead a club to try for his ninth trick, and East takes the ace of clubs and two hearts.

South cannot save himself by covering the nine with the ten of hearts. West will play the queen to force out dummy's king. When West gets in with the ace of diamonds, he returns a heart through dummy's 8-2. East can finesse with the six to drive out South's ace.